CONCRETE FORM CONSTRUCTION

CONCRETE FORM CONSTRUCTION

Cairl E. Moore

15   14

LIBRARY OF CONGRESS CATALOG CARD NUMBER: 76-3944
ISBN: 0-8273-1094-3

Printed in the United States of America
Published simultaneously in Canada
by Nelson Canada,
A division of The Thomson Corporation

NOTICE TO THE READER

Publisher does not warrant or guarantee any of the products described herein or perform any independent analysis in connection with any of the product information contained herein. Publisher does not assume, and expressly disclaims, any obligation to obtain and include information other than that provided to it by the manufacturer.

The reader is expressly warned to consider and adopt all safety precautions that might be indicated by the activities described herein and to avoid all potential hazards. By following the instructions contained herein, the reader willingly assumes all risks in connection with such instructions.

The publisher makes no representations or warranties of any kind, including but not limited to, the warranties of fitness for particular purpose or merchantability, nor are any such representations implied with respect to the material set forth herein, and the publisher takes no responsibility with respect to such material. The publisher shall not be liable for any special, consequential or exemplary damages resulting, in whole or in part, from the readers' use of, or reliance upon, this material.

DELMAR PUBLISHERS INC.
3 Columbia Circle - PO Box 15-015
Albany, NY 12212

Preface

Persons involved in building concrete forms for residential structures must be able to apply basic construction techniques, identify various soil types, establish building lines, and interpret building codes. Knowledge of tools and materials is a necessity.

CONCRETE FORM CONSTRUCTION is a comprehensive guide for the student learning concrete form construction as a trade, whether that student is enrolled in a vocational/technical, apprenticeship, or two-year college program. The text takes the student from the principles involved in analyzing and preparing the job site through actual concrete form construction of specific projects such as piers, stairs, and swimming pools.

This edition of CONCRETE FORM CONSTRUCTION, which replaces the former edition, has been completely revised to include the latest advances in the field. Step-by-step procedures encourage hands-on application of given principles. The numerous detailed drawings and photographs clearly show the practices outlined in the text. Performance objectives at the beginning of each unit stress specific skills which the student will master through careful study of the material. Review material at the end of each unit may be used to gage the individual student's understanding of the material. A separate Instructor's Guide supplies answers to these questions. Included in this edition is a new Appendix, which gives basic architectural symbols and information on the metric and English systems of measurement.

The author, Cairl E. Moore, is presently an Assistant Professor in the Industry and Technology Department at Northern Michigan University. He is a member of several professional organizations, including the American Vocational Association, the American Industrial Arts Association, and the National Association of Industrial Arts Teachers.

Other texts in the Delmar Construction: Carpentry and Woodworking series are

FRAMING AND SHEATHING
EXTERIOR AND INTERIOR TRIM
SIMPLIFIED STAIR LAYOUT
CONSTRUCTION ESTIMATING
PORTABLE POWER TOOLS
HAND WOODWORKING TOOLS

Titles in related areas include

MATHEMATICS FOR CARPENTERS
PRACTICAL PROBLEMS IN MATHEMATICS FOR CARPENTERS
BLUEPRINT READING AND SKETCHING FOR CARPENTERS — RESIDENTIAL
BUILDING TRADES BLUEPRINT READING

Contents

Section 1

Determining Foundation Requirements

Unit 1 Soil Types

OBJECTIVES

After studying this unit, the student will be able to

- identify the source for a professional soil analysis.
- compare the three basic types of soil.
- differentiate between quality and poor foundation soil.
- list solutions for problem foundation soil.

The most important factor in determining foundation requirements for a home or other small structure is the soil. Some soil is totally unsuitable for building, while other soil may be suitable but require that specific precautions be taken before the foundation is erected. Because the earth contains so many different types of soil, it is very important that the first step in preparation for building be a soil analysis. Many problems result if this step is neglected: the foundation may crack, the basement may leak, the septic tank may be ineffective, and the soil surrounding the foundation may be destroyed by erosion. All these problems which affect the foundation can be avoided if a soil analysis is made and proper precautions observed before construction begins.

SOIL SURVEYS

To help prevent problems with soil, soil engineers in the Soil Conservation Service, United States Department of Agriculture, have made soil surveys of a large percentage of the land in the United States. These surveys were made to help farmers, but they also aid builders, highway engineering departments, and anyone else who works with soil. If a soil survey has been made in the area where a builder is planning construction, the local soil conservation office or county extension service will have a soil map.

A *soil map* consists of an aerial photograph on which soil boundaries and symbols are plotted. Accompanying the map is a chart for each type of soil which provides specific information concerning their properties to a depth of about 6 feet. The survey includes a description of the soil containing such information as permeability, drainage, absorption rate, depth of various layers, and clay content. In areas where a soil survey has been taken, the soil engineer can interpret the soil map and tell the builder whether or not the soil is suitable for building and what precautions, if any, should be taken.

SOIL ANALYSIS

If the potential building site is in an area that has not been surveyed, the builder has an analysis of soil samples taken from the proposed building site, usually at 10-foot intervals.

The samples are then taken to a soil-testing laboratory which tests the soil for a fee. The results of a *soil analysis* determine the soil type present at the proposed building site. From this information, architects or engineers determine the minimum load-bearing properties per square foot of area. This enables them to decide whether or not the property is suitable for building; what type of foundation should be constructed; and what precautions, if any, should be taken.

SOIL TYPES

To accurately determine foundation specifications, the builder must understand the various classifications of soil. Each type of soil is composed of many physical and chemical properties too numerous and too specific to list here; therefore, the classifications must be general. For the scope of this text, soil is classified according to type and load-bearing capacities. There are three basic soil types: rock, virgin soil, and fill.

Rock

Rock provides the ultimate in load-bearing ability because it is relatively hard and solid, and not susceptible to shifting, weakening, or cracking by natural elements such as excessive rainfall. Rock can be classified in three categories of hardness.

- Hard rock, such as granite, is the hardest rock. It can carry in excess of 30 tons of weight per square foot (psf) of area.

- Limestone is second in hardness of the rock family and can carry up to 25 tons of weight psf.

- Shale is next in order of hardness and has a load-bearing rating of 8 to 10 tons psf.

Note: The above classifications of rock and their load-bearing capacities are valid only if the entire area upon which the foundation rests is a solid slab of rock.

Although rock is unsurpassed in its load-bearing capacity, it is extremely difficult on which to build because of the precautions that must be taken to ensure a surface which is level and free of faults.

Virgin Soils

Virgin soil is soil in its natural state. There are basically five different virgin soils: gravel, clay, loam, sand, and marsh. As with rock, the load-bearing capacity varies with each soil type.

Gravel is primarily rock mixed with various other soil materials. Its load-bearing capacities are determined by the degree of hardness of the rock, size of the *aggregates* (parts of the soil), and the composition of other materials which comprise the total soil structure. Dry, coarse gravel has a load capacity of 6 tons per square foot of area, whereas soft, fine gravel carries 4 tons per square foot of area. Gravel is stable and drains well. It is considered an excellent foundation base material.

Clay is composed mainly of hydrous aluminum silicates and other minerals. It becomes elastic and slippery when exposed to moisture; therefore, its load-bearing capacity varies greatly. Soft, wet clay carries only 1 1/2 to 2 tons per square foot. Hard, dry clay carries up to 4 tons per square foot. Because clay becomes elastic and slippery after absorbing water, it is not a good foundation base. However, foundations can be built on clay if allowances for drainage are carefully taken to stabilize the area.

Loam is a mixture of clay, silt, and sand. The load-bearing capacity of loam varies from 2 to 4 tons per square foot, according to the composition of the mixture. Loam absorbs and holds water because of the clay content. The extent to which loam changes with moisture varies with the percentage of clay in the mixture. Because of the clay content of loam, drainage precautions should be taken. Loam makes a stable foundation if the mixture compacts well and the percentage of clay is not excessive.

Sand is decomposed rock. Its quality as a foundation material depends on its degree of coarseness and the moisture content. Dry, coarse, well-compacted sand carries 3 tons per square foot; finer sand has a rating of 2 tons per square foot. Dry, coarse, well-compacted sand makes a stable foundation material. Wet sand requires that definite stabilizing precautions be taken.

Quicksand, a mixture of fine sand and loamy material, is not suitable as a foundation material. When an attempt is made to excavate in quicksand, excavations fill as quickly as the material is removed. It is possible to prepare a foundation site where there is a very limited area of quicksand, but the preparation is so expensive that it is impractical.

Marshy soil is formed by the decay of plants and other vegetable matter in sluggish water. Successive beds of decayed plants are formed under slight pressure and small cavities may develop. In some cases, these beds are so deep that their bottoms have never been reached. One method of evaluating the depth of a marsh area and determining the feasibility of erecting a structure is *test drilling.* Test drillings are made at specific intervals across the site. The depths at each interval are recorded. Once the depth has been determined and the subsoil classified according to type, foundation requirements can be specified and a cost evaluation can be made. Marshy soil of much depth involves considerable expense and is considered very dangerous as a foundation soil.

Fill

Fill is material which is no longer in its natural state. Fill is built up by the deposit of refuse materials or soil from other building sites which have been leveled. The footings for foundations are always placed on original soil. The foundation which is built directly on a fill area develops cracks or breaks because the fill material eventually settles and often leaves a cavity or void under the foundation.

The placement of footings on original soil may be accomplished by one of two methods when working on a fill area. The first method is to excavate all fill material and place the footings on the original soil. The second method is to float the building on a series of piers or pilings which carry the structural load to the original soil level. Either of these two methods can involve considerable expense but it is essential that the footings or piers rest on original soil.

The second method, floating the building on a series of piers or pilings so that it is on original soil, may be less expensive than excavating and is usually considered the more satisfactory method. The piers or pilings reach down into the original soil and serve as a pad upon which the total weight of the structure rests. By using piers or pilings, the footings are reinforced and situated so that the weight of the structure is transferred directly to the piers, which carry the weight to the original soil level.

Soil Descriptions	Foundations for Low Buildings		
	Undisturbed Soils at Building Site		Completed Fill
	Dense or Hard	Loose or Soft	
Well-graded gravel, gravel sand mixtures, little or no fines	1	1	1
Poorly graded gravels or gravel sand mixtures, little or no fines	1	2	2
Silty gravels, gravel-sand-silt mixtures	2	2	3
Clayey gravels, gravel-sand-clay mixtures	3	1	4
Well-graded sands, gravelly sands, little or no fines	1	1	2
Poorly graded sands or gravelly sands, little or no fines	1	2	4
Silty sands, sand-silt mixtures	2	2	4
Clayey sands, sand-clay mixtures	3	2	5
Inorganic silts and very fine sands, rock flour, silty or clayey fine sands or clayey silts with slight plasticity	3	3	7
Inorganic clays of low to medium plasticity, gravelly clays, sandy clays, silty clays, lean clays	3 Expansion Very Dangerous if Dry	3-5	6
Organic silts and organic silty clays of low plasticity	4 Expansion Dangerous	4	8
Inorganic silts, micaceous or diatomaceous fine sandy or silty soils, elastic silts	5	4	9
Inorganic clays of high plasticity, fat clays	5 Expansion Very Dangerous if Dry	4 Expansion Might be Dangerous	8
Organic clays of medium to high plasticity, organic silts	6 Expansion Dangerous	5	10
Peat and other highly organic soils	7	N.S.*	N.S.
Low buildings are defined as buildings up to and including three stories. Numbers in each column are a rating of suitability with #1 being the most suitable. The symbol N.S. indicates that the soil is generally considered "not suitable."			

* Not Suitable; should not be used.

Fig. 1-1 Soil Data. (*Engineering Soil Classification for Residential Developments,* U.S. Government Printing Office, Washington, D.C., pp. 49-50.) **This chart indicates whether soil is stable enough for a foundation.** Courtesy of the Federal Housing Administration

The expense involved in building foundations in a fill area often makes it less desirable than the construction of a foundation under normal conditions; however, placing a foundation directly on a fill area is not recommended. A foundation can be safely placed in a fill area if the original soil level is a quality foundation material and the cost of situating the foundation on the original soil is not too great.

These soil classifications are very general. The soil in a given area is rarely one soil; most likely, it is a combination of many soils. Figure 1-1 shows the fifteen most commonly found soil materials. It is used as a soil guide by the Federal Housing Administration as an acceptable standard for residential developers in determining the suitability of an area for residential developments. The builder can obtain a soil survey that indicates whether the area under consideration can be developed economically.

In terms of soil, the builder is usually most concerned with the foundation, the sewer disposal systems if the construction site is outside the metropolitan sewer district's service area, and the potential danger resulting from frost penetration. In these terms, number one in figure 1-1 is the most desirable soil combination. The higher the number in the chart is, the less desirable the soil combination is.

Recognizing soil quality is the first step to a sound foundation. For this reason, a soil analysis and advice should be obtained from the soil conservation office or county extension service before any foundation is erected. This service is available to all builders, whether they are located in a city or in a rural area.

APPLICATION

A. Select the best answer from the choices offered to complete the statement or answer the question.

1. The most important factor in determining foundation requirements for a home or small structure is

   a. cost.   c. soil.
   b. type of foundation.   d. foundation material.

2. An aerial photograph on which soil boundaries and symbols are plotted is a (an)

   a. boundary map.   c. builder's map.
   b. soil map.   d. soil analysis.

3. Which of the following is *not* a basic soil type?

   a. rock   c. virgin soil
   b. sand   d. fill

4. A soil map and chart for each type of soil has been developed by soil scientists in the Soil Conservation Service which is under the

   a. Department of Agriculture.
   b. Department of Interior.
   c. Department of State.
   d. Department of Health, Education and Welfare.

5. Rock mixed with various other soil materials is

   a. clay.   c. gravel.
   b. fill.   d. sand.

6. Footings for foundations on a fill area should be
   a. placed on original soil.
   b. well drained.
   c. thicker than footings on virgin soil.
   d. determined by the type of fill material.

7. If a soil map for a potential building site is not available, the builder should
   a. ask the Soil Conservation Office to compile a soil map of the area.
   b. take a soil sample and determine the soil type by feeling the texture.
   c. ask the people in the area what the soil type is.
   d. have a soil analysis made by a soil-testing laboratory.

8. The ultimate soil type in load-bearing ability is
   a. rock.   c. shale.
   b. virgin soil.   d. fill.

9. For a soil analysis of a proposed building site, samples should be taken at
   a. 5-foot intervals.
   b. 10-foot intervals.
   c. at each corner of the foundation.
   d. directly under the center of the foundation.

10. A virgin soil which is a poor foundation material because it becomes elastic and slippery when exposed to moisture is
    a. fill.   c. loam.
    b. sand.   d. clay.

B. Complete each statement with the correct word or words.

1. Soil material which is no longer in its natural state is known as _____.

2. Soil in its natural state is known as _____.

3. The branch of the United States Department of Agriculture which provides soil surveys is the _____.

4. The load-bearing capacity of clay varies greatly since it becomes elastic and slippery when exposed to _____.

5. A foundation can be built on fill soil if the foundation is floated on a series of _____ or _____ which are constructed on original soil.

6. Loam is a mixture of three materials, which are _____.

7. An excellent foundation material which is stable and drains well is _____.

8. Of the three basic soil types, the type which provides the ultimate in load-bearing ability is _____.

9. When building a foundation on loam, drainage precautions must be taken because of the _____ content.

10. The quality of sand as a foundation material depends on the degree of two things, _____ and _____.

Unit 2   Footing Requirements

OBJECTIVES

After studying this unit, the student will be able to

- determine standard footing sizes for specific projects.
- identify types of loads on a house foundation.
- figure the total load weight of a specific structure.

After the builder has determined that the soil at the proposed building site is suitable for a foundation base, the proper footing size must be determined. A *footing* is a wide concrete base on which foundation walls or piers rest. Footings are used to distribute the structural weight over a larger area, resulting in a more stable foundation. There is a simple, standard method of determining footing size which is sufficient for most residential buildings. However, the standard footing is not always workable if the structure is unusually large or if it is erected on poor foundation soil.

DETERMINING THE STANDARD FOOTING SIZE

Under normal building conditions in residential construction, the standard footing size is sufficient. The standard footing is twice as wide and the same depth as the wall is thick, with the wall centered on the footing, figure 2-1. For example, poured foundation walls for frame construction are usually 8 inches thick; therefore, the footing is 16 inches wide and 8 inches deep with a 4-inch projection on each side of the foundation wall. Poured foundations for masonry walls are usually 10 to 12 inches thick; therefore, the footing is 20 to 24 inches wide and 10 to 12 inches deep with a 5- to 6-inch projection of each side of the foundation wall as shown in figure 2-1. This is a generally accepted method of determining footing size under normal building conditions; however, the builder should always consult local building codes for minimum requirements.

DETERMINING THE CUSTOM FOOTING SIZE

The standard footing size is not always sufficient if the foundation is being erected on poor foundation soil or if the building is unusually large so that the foundation load is greater. Because of this, the builder should also know how to figure a specific footing size by considering the structural load and the soil-bearing strength.

Structural Load

Structural load is the total weight that foundation footings must support at any given

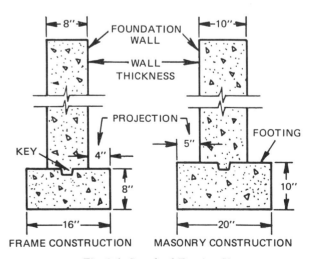

Fig. 2-1 Standard Footing Size.

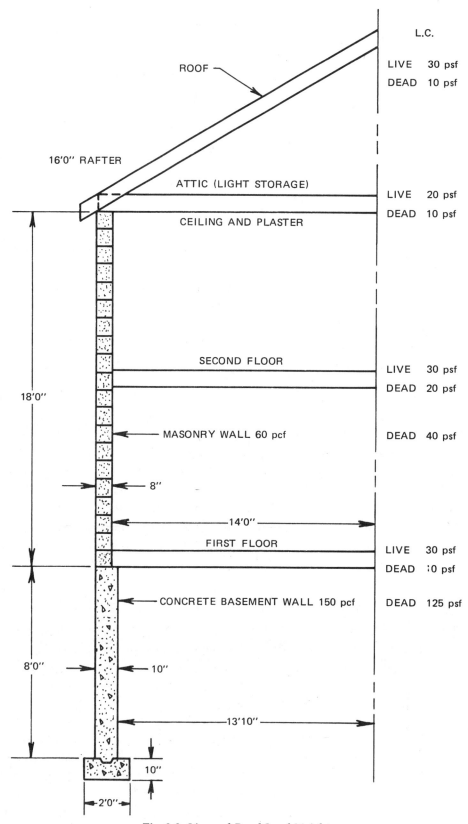

Fig. 2-2 Live and Dead Load Weight.

time. Two types of loads must be considered when determining the total structural load, the live loads and the dead loads. A *live load* is the sum of all moving and variable loads that may be placed upon a structure. The live roof load varies according to the geographical area in which the structure is located. For example, the live roof load of a structure in Michigan is much heavier than the live roof load of an identical structure in Florida, because of the heavy snow accumulation in winter.

A *dead load* is the total weight of the permanent, stationary structural elements of the building. To determine the total struc-

Soils	Weight per Sq. Ft.
Rock-Granite	30 tons
Limestone (Compacted)	25 tons
Shale (Soft Rock)	8-10 tons
Gravel (Dry, Coarse)	6 tons
Gravel (Soft, Coarse)	4-6 tons
Clay (Dry, Thick Beds)	4 tons
Clay (Dry, Soft Beds)	1-1 1/2 tons
Sand (Clean, Dry, and Confined)	2 tons
Sand (Coarse, Compact)	3 tons
Earth [Solid and Dry (Natural)]	4 tons

Fig. 2-3 Bearing Strength of Soils.

tural load, the weight of the various levels (components) of the structure must be determined so that the total weight per square foot of area can be figured. Figure 2-2 gives the generally acceptable construction weights of the various levels of a typical structure. *Note:* Because requirements differ in various areas, local building codes should always be consulted for live and dead weight specifications for specific areas.

Load-Bearing Strength of Soil

The second factor which must be considered when figuring the footing size is the *load-bearing strength* of the soil. The load-bearing strength is the weight per square foot which a specific soil is able to support, figure 2-3. For example, dry, coarse gravel is an excellent foundation soil which can support 6 tons per square foot. When a foundation is being erected on dry, coarse gravel, a standard footing is more than sufficient. Soft clay is not a good foundation base since it supports only 1 to 1 1/2 tons per square foot. However, a foundation can be safely erected on soft clay if the proper size footings are poured and if the necessary drainage precautions are taken.

Making The Specific Calculation

The builder determines the required footing size by adding the live and dead weight loads to obtain the total weight load that the footings are required to support. The size of the footing is then determined by dividing the total load of the structure by the load-bearing strength of the soil on which the structure is to be placed. A step-by-step calculation follows for the building in figure 2-2. Assume that the building is situated on soft clay.

Roof Area. The live load (snow load) for the building in figure 2-2 is 30 psf (pounds per square foot). The dead load for the roof is 10 psf. Therefore, the combined live and dead load for this roof is 40 psf. The rafter length is 16 feet. All the weight is carried by the outside wall. To obtain the weight load of the roof, multiply the rafter length by the combined live and dead roof load: 16 feet x 40 psf = 640 pounds per linear foot. The result is a 640-pound load to be placed on each linear foot of each exterior wall.

Second Floor Ceiling. The dead load of the second floor ceiling in figure 2-2 is 10 psf. The total structure width is 28 feet. Half the weight is resting on each exterior sidewall. To obtain the load weight of the second floor ceiling which rests on each exterior sidewall, divide the total width by 2: 28 feet ÷ 2 = 14. This indicates that half the second floor ceiling weight is placed on each exterior sidewall. The width is then multiplied by the weight: 14 x 10 psf = 140. Therefore, there is a 140-pound second floor ceiling load on each linear foot of the exterior wall.

Second Floor. The live load for the second floor in figure 2-2 is 30 psf. The dead load for the second floor, floor joists, and the first-floor ceiling is 20 psf. Therefore, the combined live and dead load for the second floor is 50 psf. To obtain the weight which rests on each exterior wall, again divide the total width of the structure by 2: 28 ÷ 2 = 14. Then multiply the width by the combined live and dead load: 14 x 50 psf = 700. The second-floor load is 700 pounds per linear foot of exterior wall.

First Floor. The live load for the first floor in figure 2-2 is 30 psf; the dead load is 10 psf. The combined live and dead load is 40 psf. Half the first floor or 14 feet rests on each exterior wall. To obtain the weight of the first floor resting on each exterior wall, multiply the width by the combined weight: 14 x 40 psf = 560. The first-floor load is 560 pounds per linear foot of exterior wall.

Masonry Wall. The dead load of the masonry wall in figure 2-2 is 60 pcf (pounds per cubic foot). The weight for one linear foot of 8-foot wall must be figured. To do this, multiply the pounds per cubic foot by the size of the wall: 60 pcf x 8/12 = 40. The product is then multiplied by the wall height: 40 x 18 = 720. The masonry wall load is 720 pounds for each linear foot of wall space.

Basement Wall (Concrete). The average dead weight of concrete is 150 pounds per cubic foot. The weight for a 10-inch concrete wall must be figured. Multiply the pounds per cubic foot by the wall thickness: 150 pcf x 10/12 = 125. To obtain the dead weight per linear foot of basement wall, multiply the wall height by 125 pounds: 8 x 125 = 1000 pounds per linear foot of concrete basement wall space.

Total Structural Load. The total load resting on each linear foot of the footing is determined by adding the totals obtained in steps 1 through 6: 640 + 140 + 700 + 560 + 720 + 1000 = 3760. The cumulative structural load is 3760 pounds. If light attic storage is assumed for the structure as it is in figure 2-2, 280 pounds must be added for the live attic load. There are 4040 pounds resting on each linear foot of the footing.

The Final Step. This step is the determining factor in the footing size. To obtain the footing size, divide the total structural weight by the weight that the soil on which the structure is to be placed can support. The building in this example is being constructed on soft clay, which supports only 1 to 1 1/2 tons per square foot of area. The total structural weight of the house in figure 2-2 is 4040 pounds.

To obtain the footing size, divide the total structural weight by 2000 pounds (use the lower weight to ensure a footing which is sufficiently large): 4040 ÷ 2000; this gives the size required to support the structural load. The answer, 2.02, indicates that 2 square feet of area are needed to fully support the total weight of each linear foot of foundation wall. Therefore, the footing should be 2 feet wide. The remainder of the figure, .02 is dropped since it is insignificant in relation to the footing size.

The compressive strength, or weight-bearing strength, of concrete is far beyond most load-bearing strengths. The footing thickness is determined by a standard method. Under this method, the thickness of the footing is one-half of the required width of the footing and is never less than the thickness of the wall which supports the building. In this example, the footing is 2 feet wide as figured and 1 foot thick (the thickness of the footing is one-half the width).

APPLICATION

A. Complete each statement with the correct word or words.

1. The purpose of footings is to distribute the _____ of a building over a larger area, resulting in a more stable foundation.

2. The ratio of wall thickness to footing width is _____.

3. The footing projection on each side of a foundation wall is equal to _____ the wall thickness.

4. The standard thickness for a foundation wall of a frame structure is _____.

5. The footing thickness for a 10-inch foundation wall is _____.

6. The two types of loads found in a residential structure are _____ and _____.

7. The total of all moving and variable loads that may be placed on a building is known as the _____.

8. The total weight of the permanent, stationary elements of a building is known as the _____.

9. The two factors which must be considered when calculating footing size are the _____ and _____.

10. Builders should always consult the _____ for minimum footing requirements.

B. Perform a step-by-step calculation of the structural load of the building on page 12 and determine the footing size. Assume that the building is located on soft clay.

1. roof area _____

2. second-floor ceiling _____

3. second floor _____

4. first floor _____

5. masonry wall _____

6. basement wall _____

7. total structural load _____

8. load-bearing strength _____

9. footing size _____ x _____

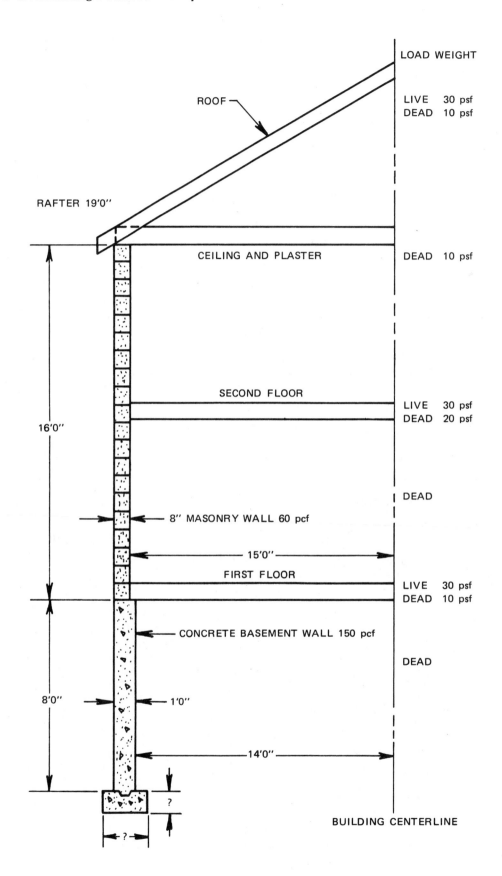

LOAD WEIGHT

LIVE   30 psf
DEAD   10 psf

ROOF

RAFTER 19'0''

CEILING AND PLASTER

DEAD   10 psf

SECOND FLOOR

LIVE   30 psf
DEAD   20 psf

16'0''

DEAD

8'' MASONRY WALL 60 pcf

15'0''

FIRST FLOOR

LIVE   30 psf
DEAD   10 psf

CONCRETE BASEMENT WALL 150 pcf

DEAD

8'0''   1'0''

14'0''

?

?

BUILDING CENTERLINE

Unit 3 Frost Line Precautions

OBJECTIVES

After studying this unit, the student will be able to

- define the term *frost line*.
- list the factors affecting frost line depth.
- explain the effects of frost line penetration upon the foundation.
- list the precautions that should be taken to prevent heaving.

It is very important that the builder understand the meaning of frost line and how it affects foundation work. The *frost line* is defined as the depth to which soil freezes. The frost line varies according to geographical area, figure 3-1. Local building codes should always be consulted to obtain the frost line depth of each particular area.

Frost penetration occurs when moisture which is present in the soil freezes. The frost depth does not necessarily increase with more northern locations. In addition to the temperature of the area, the soil type must be considered, figure 3-2. For example, a dry, porous soil such as gravel has a very shallow frost line penetration because it drains very well. A wet, clay soil has a deeper frost line penetration because it absorbs and holds moisture. Figure 3-2 shows the wide variation in frost line penetration in various soil types.

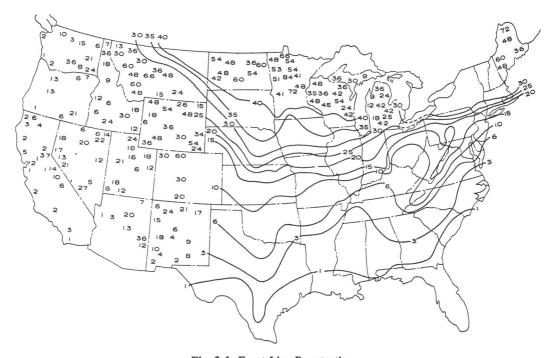

Fig. 3-1 Frost Line Penetration.
Courtesy of the United States Department of Commerce

13

Soil Descriptions	Potential Frost Action	
	Disturbed Soils	Undisturbed Soils
Well-graded gravel, gravel sand mixtures, little or no fines	1	1
Poorly graded gravels or gravel-sand mixtures, little or no fines	1	3
Silty gravels, gravel-sand-silt mixtures	2-3	9
Clayey gravels, gravel-sand-silt clay mixtures	2-3	5
Well-graded sands, gravelly sands little or no fines	1	2
Poorly graded sands or gravelly sands, little or no fines	1	4
Silty sands, sand-silt mixtures	4	10
Clayey sands, sand-clay mixtures	4	6
Inorganic silts and very fine sands, rock flour, silty or clayey fines, sands or clayey silts with slight plasticity	3-5	11
Inorganic clays of low to medium plasticity, gravelly clays, sandy clays, silty clays, lean clays	3-4	7
Organic silts and organic silty clays of low plasticity	3-4	12
Inorganic silts, micaceous or diatomaceous fine sandy or silty soils, elastic silts	3-5	13
Inorganic clays of high plasticity, fat clays	3	8
Organic clays of medium to high plasticity, organic silts	3	12
Peat and other highly organic silts	2	N.S.*

*Not suitable.

Fig. 3-2 Soil types and potential frost action. Numbers in the columns are ratings of desirability, with number 1 being the most desirable. The higher the number is, the less desirable the soil is.
Courtesy of the Federal Housing Administration

There is an equally wide variation in the average depth of frost penetration in various cold areas with similar temperature ranges. For example, one area in Michigan's upper peninsula has a 9-inch frost penetration, while the adjacent area has a frost line depth of 30 inches. The first area mentioned has only a 9-inch frost line depth simply because the area has a higher elevation with a coarse, sandy soil which drains well and remains relatively dry; therefore, the frost depth is comparatively shallow. There are areas in northern Idaho and Montana that have only a 6-inch frost penetration while areas in middle Illinois and Missouri, where the temperature is not nearly as cold, have a frost line penetration depth of 25 inches. Obviously, weather alone does not control the frost line penetration. Consulting local building codes for frost line penetration depth is always a necessity.

HEAVING

In construction, *heaving* is the raising and lowering of a structure. Usually, structures that are built with the footings above the frost line are subject to heaving. When soil freezes, it expands, pushing the structure upward and out of the soil. When the soil thaws, the structure settles to its original level or sometimes lower, depending upon the moisture level of the soil. As a result of this raising and lowering, the structure may shift positions or settle unevenly, causing damage to the footings and foundation walls.

The Prevention of Heaving

The best way to prevent heaving is to place the footings of a structure below the frost line. In this way, the footings serve as structural anchors. This prevents the structure from shifting, and eliminates the possibility of damage from heaving.

A second precaution which should be taken to prevent heaving is to provide an adequate drainage system. This is most important in soil containing clay. To be certain there is adequate drainage, drain tile is installed at the base of the foundation to provide a means of quick removal of moisture before it accumulates and saturates the area around the building site. A drainage system is not always necessary if the foundation soil is a coarse, dry soil which drains rapidly; however, an adequate drainage system is needed with most soil types.

Figure 3-3 shows the proper placement of footings and drain tile so that the danger of heaving is eliminated. A standard 8-inch concrete block foundation wall and an 8-inch poured concrete foundation wall have footings placed below the frost line and properly installed drain tile. There are two coats of portland cement plaster 1/4 inch thick and a bituminous coating which act as waterproofing to ensure that the crawl space underneath the house remains dry. (The application of the plaster is known as *parging*.) The portland cement plaster should be used to seal the walls if the water table or moisture level is high. However, many builders eliminate the portland cement plaster if the foundation soil is well drained. The application of the bituminous coating should never be eliminated from either the poured concrete or the concrete block foundation wall.

The footing is always placed below the frost line; the depth of the footing varies according to the depth of the frost penetration. For example, in an area with a 10-inch frost line depth, the footings must be placed so that the top of the footing is below the 10-inch depth. Some structures

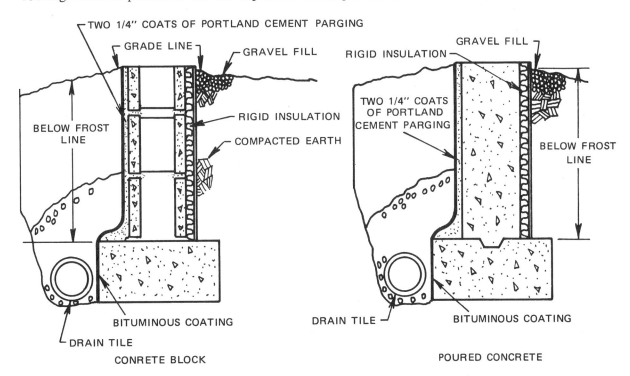

Fig. 3-3 Standard Foundation (Footings Below Frost Line).

with no basements may have footings that are set as deep as the footings for structures equipped with a basement.

Figure 3-4 illustrates the placement of a footing which supports a poured concrete basement wall. The basement wall is waterproofed with two coats of portland cement plaster and a bituminous coating. The drain tile is installed so that excessive moisture is eliminated. Footings are placed below the frost line.

Figure 3-5 illustrates how a slab foundation should be placed for an area that has little or no frost line penetration. Footings are not required for a slab foundation under these soil conditions; however, the slab should be set on a dry base of gravel to ensure quick drainage of the area, thereby providing stable soil.

Figure 3-6 illustrates how a slab foundation should be placed when the area frost line penetration is deep and the moisture level is high. Footings are required for slab foundations when the frost line penetration is deep,

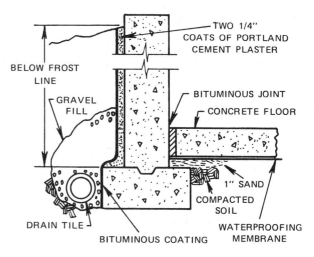

Fig. 3-4 Standard Foundation (Footings Below Frost Line Supporting Poured Concrete Basement Wall)

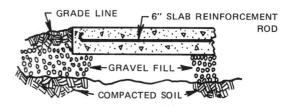

Fig. 3-5 Slab Foundation (Dry Area; No Frost Line Penetration)

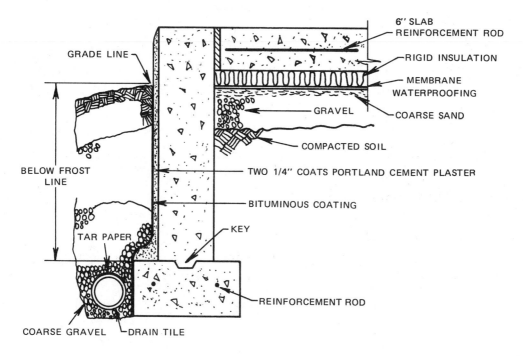

Fig. 3-6 Slab Foundation (Wet Area; Deep Frost Penetration).

as illustrated in the figure. Otherwise, heaving results, thereby causing cracks in the foundation. The footings are placed below the frost line with a properly installed drainage system. The foundation wall is waterproofed with two 1/4-inch coats of portland cement plaster and a bituminous coating. Membrane waterproofing is applied to the slab, which is placed on a layer of gravel and a layer of sand. These precautions should eliminate excessive moisture under the slab and prevent heaving.

The builder can erect a stable foundation that does not heave by observing certain precautions, such as placing the footings below the frost line and providing an adequate drainage system. Initially, the builder must be familiar with the soil conditions and frost line depth of that area.

APPLICATION

Complete each statement with the correct word or words.

1. The frost line is the level or depth to which soil _____.

2. The two factors which determine the frost penetration depth are _____ and _____.

3. Frost penetration occurs when the _____ which is present in the soil freezes.

4. The raising and lowering of a structure which occurs after soil freezes is known as _____.

5. Two precautions which may be taken to prevent heaving are to place the foundation footings below the _____ and to provide an adequate _____.

6. When a foundation footing is below the frost line, the footing serves as a (an) _____ to prevent heaving.

7. The depth at which the footing is placed is determined by the _____.

8. Is frost penetration deeper in wet clay, coarse gravel, or dry sand?
   _____

9. Using figure 3-1, determine the approximate frost line depth for the following locations.
   a. Northernmost Maine
   b. Southernmost California
   c. Miami, Florida

10. Which of the following types of soil drains well and is not subject to deep frost penetration: dry sand, wet clay, or coarse gravel? _____

Unit 4 Drainage Systems

OBJECTIVES

After studying this unit, the student will be able to

- state the purpose of drainage systems.
- compare installation procedures of an adequate drainage system for each type of foundation.
- list the steps involved in waterproofing a foundation.

The soil on which foundations are placed determines whether or not a drainage system is necessary. If the soil is dry, coarse gravel which drains well, there is no need for a drainage system. Most soils, however, absorb and retain moisture in varying degrees. If there is any doubt concerning the drainage properties of a foundation soil, perimeter drain tile, or drainage pipe, is installed.

Drainage systems serve a dual purpose. As previously discussed, adequate drainage systems help prevent heaving by quickly removing excessive moisture from the foundation area so that there is no moisture in the soil to freeze. Drainage systems also aid in waterproofing the foundation itself.

Different foundation types require different procedures in the installation of drainage systems.

STANDARD FOUNDATIONS

A standard foundation consists of a foundation wall and a footing which is constructed to the thickness and width required to support the load weight of the structure, figure 4-1. The poured concrete or concrete masonry wall is centered on the footing and anchored by the key. The standard foundation wall and the basement or crawl space under the house can be adequately protected from moisture through two basic measures.

The first involves the application of two 1/4-inch coats of cement plaster on the exterior face of the foundation wall from the grade line down and over the footing. The cement plaster should be applied before

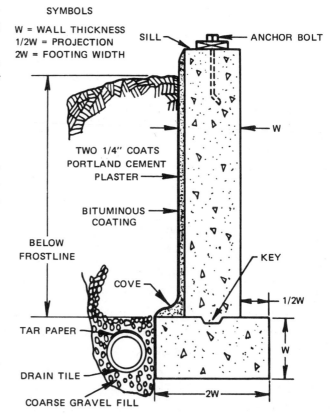

SYMBOLS

W = WALL THICKNESS
1/2W = PROJECTION
2W = FOOTING WIDTH

SILL — ANCHOR BOLT

TWO 1/4" COATS PORTLAND CEMENT PLASTER

BITUMINOUS COATING

BELOW FROSTLINE

COVE

TAR PAPER

DRAIN TILE

COARSE GRAVEL FILL

W

KEY

1/2W

W

2W

Fig. 4-1 Standard Foundation with Placement of Drain Tile.

Fig. 4-2 Hot bituminous coating sprayed on a section of concrete wall to the grade line. Courtesy of Meyer Foundation Company, Incorporated.

Fig. 4-3 Flexible perforated plastic drain tile. This tile can be obtained in lengths up to 250 feet. Courtesy of Mid-Missouri Company

the tile is positioned. To prevent water from collecting in the angle where the footing and wall join, a cove of cement plaster should be formed so that the water is able to drain. The first coat of cement plaster should be applied to a clean, moist surface. Before the cement plaster hardens, the surface should be roughened with a wire brush to prepare a bonding surface for the second coat. The first coat is allowed to harden at least 24 hours. After the first coat of cement plaster has hardened, the second coat is applied. The surface should be moist when the cement plaster is applied. This coat should be kept moist approximately 48 hours so that the cement cures properly.

The second step in waterproofing the foundation wall is to apply two coats of hot bituminous coating or asphalt waterproofing. The coating should be brushed or sprayed on and allowed to dry. When the first coat is dry, apply the second coat.

If the soil is porous with little or no clay and drains well, the poured concrete wall may be waterproofed by using only two coats of hot bituminous or asphalt coating, figure 4-2.

After the foundation walls have been waterproofed with cement plaster and hot bituminous coating, the drain tile is positioned. Perimeter drain tile may be clay tile, rigid plastic, or flexible plastic. The flexible plastic drain tile is a continuous, flexible tile which requires no couplings, figure 4-3. Figure 4-4 shows the perforated clay drainage pipe and the various dimensions of the pipe.

Drainpipe is laid at the base of the footing with open joints covered so that earth and silt are prevented from entering but water is allowed to penetrate. The water is carried to a catch basin away from the foundation, figure 4-5. A *catch basin* (or *dry well*) is an area excavated and filled with loose gravel and covered with topsoil. The catch basin provides an emergency storage area for large accumulations of water. In cities or urban areas where storm sewers are available, the perimeter drainage system may, with a permit, be connected to the street storm sewer system.

Proper placement of drainage tile is critical in determining whether or not the drainage system is functional. The perforated tile is placed around the outside edge of the footings as shown

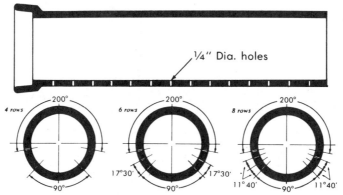

Holes are staggered in 6 and 8 row pipe.

Dimensions of Perforated Pipe

Normal Size (in.)	Normal Laying Length (ft)	Rows	Perforations Per Row			
			3 (ft)	4 (ft)	5 (ft)	6 (ft)
4	3, 4	4	11	14		
6	3, 4, 5	4	11	14	18	
8	5	4		14	18	
10	5	6			18	
12	5	6			18	
15	5, 6	6			18	22
18	5, 6	8			18	22
21	5, 6	8			18	22
24	5, 6	8			18	22

Fig. 4-4 Perforated drainpipe and specifications chart.
Courtesy of W. S. Dickey Clay Manufacturing Company

in figure 4-1. The soil is firmly compacted with a minimum of 1 inch of washed gravel or crushed stone underneath the tile. The tile is positioned so that it slopes 1 inch for every 12 to 20 feet of tile. The tile sections are placed about 1/4 inch apart, with the tile joints covered to prevent silt from entering the tile. Tile joints may be covered with tar paper, but a more efficient method is a specially designed snap coupling with a slit in the bottom.

After the drain tile is installed, the surrounding area is filled with crushed stone or washed gravel to a minimum depth of 1 foot. If the soil is a wet clay or silt soil, the area should be backfilled with a porous material to 6 or 8 inches from the grade line. This provides a means of filtering soil particles from the water so that the drain tile does not fill with silt and become ineffective.

PIER FOUNDATIONS

Pier foundations are used in areas with fill soil and in low areas which have high water tables, causing the area underneath the structure to be wet. *Pier foundations* consist of foundation

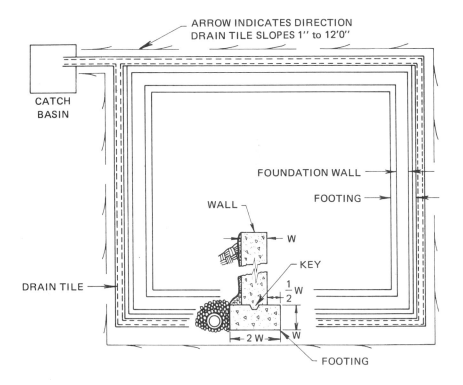

Fig. 4-5 Standard Foundation With Placement of Drain Tile and Catch Basin.

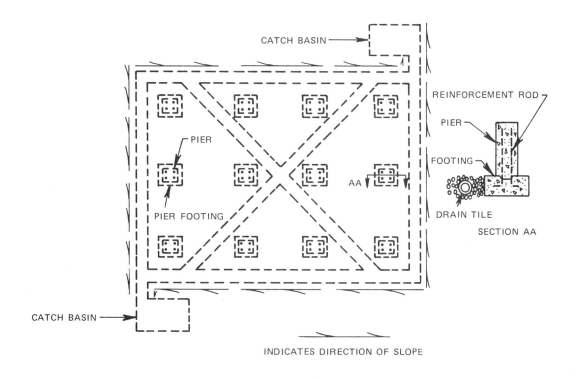

Fig. 4-6 Drainage System for Pier Foundation

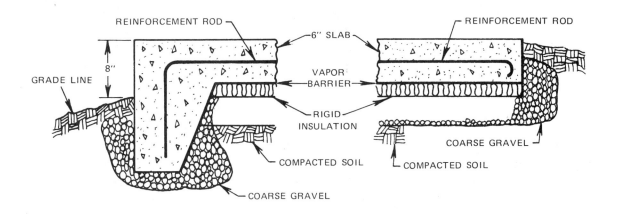

Fig. 4-7 Slab Foundation (Dry, Well-drained Area).

footings with concrete columns centered upon the footing, figure 4-6 (Section AA). The footings are constructed according to the size required to support the load weight of the structure. The footings, as always are installed below the frost line.

Specific care must be taken in waterproofing the walls of pier foundations. The waterproofing procedure is the same as that for standard foundations, which involves the application of two 1/4-inch coats of cement plaster and two coats of hot bituminous or asphalt coating.

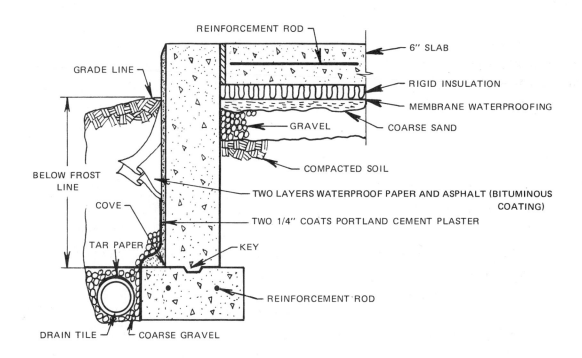

Fig. 4-8 Slab Foundation (Wet Area; Deep Frost Penetration).

The drainage tile and catch basin for pier foundations are installed by the same method as standard foundations. However, because the area which requires a pier foundation is usually an area that is particularly susceptible to water retention, more drain tile is laid diagonally across the foundation area, as well as around the perimeter. The backfill for a pier foundation drainage system consists of a porous material filled to 6 or 8 inches from the grade line.

SLAB FOUNDATIONS

The slab foundation consists of a reinforced layer of concrete placed directly over a well-compacted gravel base, figure 4-7. The slab foundation may also have supporting members placed directly under the load-bearing walls to provide adequate weight support. Slab foundations in dry areas may not require drain tile to prevent undue settling if natural drainage is adequate and there is no frost line penetration.

In wet areas and in areas with deep frost penetration, the slab foundation should have an adequate drainage system to prevent heaving and to keep excessive moisture from the slab. The slab foundation should have footings which are poured below the frost line, with a foundation wall extending to the top of the slab, figure 4-8. The foundation should be covered with two 1/4-inch coats of cement plaster applied in the same way as for a standard foundation. In addition, two layers of waterproofed paper or builder's felt saturated with asphalt are placed around the foundation. It extends from above the grade line, across the top of the footing, and back up the inside of the foundation wall. At this point, it is sealed to the waterproofing membrane that is placed directly over a layer of coarse sand and directly beneath the rigid installation.

After the builder's felt has been sealed to the waterproofed membrane, the drain tile may be installed around the perimeter. The drain tile is installed following the same procedures that are used on standard foundation. The perforated drain tile is placed on a bed of crushed stone at least 1 inch deep and sloped at least 1 inch every 12 to 20 feet. The tiles are placed approximately 1/4 inch apart and the connections either covered with tar paper or snap connectors. The drain tile is then covered with at least 1 foot of crushed stone. As is the case in the standard foundation, the drain tile should lead to a catch basin or to a storm sewer. If these precautions are followed, the foundation should remain dry and should not be subject to heaving.

APPLICATION

A.   Complete each statement with the correct word or words.

1. Drainage systems help prevent _____ and aid in _____ the foundation by providing means for the rapid removal of excess water.

2. The exterior face of a poured concrete wall in a relatively well-drained area is coated with _____.

3. A masonry block wall must have two coats of _____ and two coats of _____ to provide waterproofing.

4. To prevent water from collecting in the angle where the footing and wall join, a _____ of cement plaster is formed.

5. The first coat of cement plaster must be _____ to prepare a good bonding surface for the second coat.

6. So that it cures properly, the second coat of cement plaster is kept moist approximately _____ hours.

7. List the three types of perimeter drain tile.

_____

_____

_____

8. A catch basin provides a (an) _____ for large accumulations of water.

9. There should be a minimum of _____ of washed gravel or crushed stone underneath drain tile.

10. A drainage system for a pier foundation differs from a standard foundation drainage system in that drain tile is placed _____ across the foundation as well as around the perimeter.

11. A pier foundation is used in _____ soil.

12. A cavity or hole filled with loose gravel or rock and covered with topsoil is known as a (an) _____.

13. A (An) _____ foundation consists of a reinforced layer of concrete placed directly over a well-compacted gravel base.

14. A slab foundation is covered with two 1/4-inch coats of _____ applied in the same way as for a standard foundation.

15. After drain tile is installed around a standard foundation, the surrounding area is filled with _____ or _____ to a minimum depth of 1 foot.

B. Label the parts of the standard foundation shown in the cross-sectional view below.

1. _____
2. _____
3. _____
4. _____
5. _____
6. _____
7. _____
8. _____
9. _____
10. _____
11. _____
12. _____
13. _____
14. _____

Section 2

Locating The Structure

Unit 5   Building Codes

OBJECTIVES

After studying this unit the student will be able to

- interpret local building codes.
- identify specifics of construction which must conform to local building codes.
- list the steps involved in obtaining a building permit.

Residential construction must meet certain standards as set forth in the local building codes. *Building codes* are restrictions and regulations established by local governing agencies to ensure acceptable construction standards. They cover features of major construction, such as the foundation, general construction (carpentry), and electrical and plumbing work. Building codes are designed to protect the homeowner or builder against inferior quality in the structure and to provide specified standards for the community. All incorporated communities have building codes.

To protect the building and the property owners, as well as the community itself, building codes set quality material and construction standards. Because of the wide variation in building codes, every builder or prospective owner should consult the codes before a structure is designed. After the codes have been checked and the structure designed, the application for the building permit is made.

Before a structure is designed for a particular building lot, the prospective homeowner or builder should contact the building inspector's office where the local building codes can be obtained. Because it is so difficult to keep local building codes current with the latest construction materials and procedures, some organizations now provide current model building codes that have been adopted by many communities, such as the NATIONAL BUILDING CODE, published by the American Insurance Company, and the UNIFORM BUILDING CODE, published by the International Conference of Building Officials. This organization prepares annual revisions of the code. A third model building code, the BASIC BUILDING CODE, is published by the Building Officials Conference of America. The Southern Building Code Conference has prepared a model building code known as the SOUTHERN STANDARD BUILDING CODE, for use in southern states only. These model building codes help to eliminate the problems which local communities face in keeping their building codes current with modern construction procedures. Not all communities, however, have accepted the model codes.

In addition to the building codes within an established city or incorporated area, some states have basic uniform building codes which govern residential construction outside the jurisdiction of the local city or township.

SEPARATE REGULATIONS

Although most communities have a building code which covers all phases of construction, the builder may find that in some areas, there are separate restrictions for each of the various stages of construction. For example, the builder may have to secure a set of regulations for the basic construction, foundation work, electrical code, and the plumbing and sewer regulations. If the regulations are contained in one building code, they can usually be obtained from the local building inspector's office. However, if each set of regulations is separate, they are usually obtained from various specific departments of the city.

In rural developments, some specifications may be available only from state offices within the county where the site is located, such as regulation governing the water supply. If the water source is a private well on the individual's property, the state health department provides the specifications for the construction of the well. If the builder is developing in a rural area, a special effort must be made to determine the availability of services to the building site. Often, services are available but at a considerable cost to the builder since the site is out of the normal service range.

FOUNDATION REGULATIONS

The builder or contractor who is erecting the foundation must investigate the building code regulations which apply specifically to the foundation work. The frost line depth should always be checked to ensure that the footings are poured deeply enough to prevent heaving. Local building codes should also be reviewed to determine live and dead weight structural loads so that the proper footing size can be determined. Minimum footing size and depth is specified in building codes of specific communities.

Building codes also have special regulations concerning foundation walls. Most building codes specify that foundation walls must be at least 8 inches thick. They also usually specify a minimum distance between the grade line and the top of the foundation wall. Anchoring methods may also be regulated, especially if the structure is being built in an area which experiences severe weather conditions.

The depth of the basement floor below the grade line must also be considered when erecting the foundation. The Federal Housing Administration specifies that the floor level of any habitable room cannot be more than 48 inches below the grade level of the exterior wall. This applies only to rooms designed for year-round occupancy and not for rooms such as utility rooms, recreation rooms, and bathrooms.

Most local building codes meet or exceed Federal Housing Administration minimum standards. Adherence to Federal Housing Administration minimum standards does not exempt a builder from following local building codes.

Building codes vary from community to community. Some are very stringent; others have few restrictions. By necessity, geographical conditions have a bearing on the building codes of a community. For example, footings must be deeper in northern sections. A heavier dead roof load must be considered in certain areas because of heavy snow accumulation. Anchoring methods must be more substantial in areas which experience hurricanes.

THE BUILDING PERMIT

Before construction of a building can begin, a building permit must be obtained. To obtain a building permit, a formal application, figure 5-1, must be filed with the local building officials. The application may be filed by either the builder or the prospective owner. A complete set of drawings and specifications for the proposed structure must accompany the application. The plans are reviewed by the building officials to determine whether or not they meet building code regulations. If the plans and specifications meet

Fig. 5-1 Application for Building Permit.
Courtesy Marquette City Hall, Marquette, Michigan

Builder's License No. _____

APPLICATION FOR A BUILDING PERMIT

TO THE BUILDING INSPECTOR OF THE CITY OF MARQUETTE:

I, _____ , make the following statement for _____
of _____ who proposes to construct, alter, or convert, as specified herein, upon the following land, viz: Give *Légal* description Lot, Block and Subdivision:

Specifications are as follows: Cost $_____; Dimensions, Main part: _____ ft.
Wings: _____ ft.; Roof Material _____; Chimneys,
No. _____; Size: _____; Material _____;
Heating _____; Lighting: _____; Sewage Disposal _____;
Architect: _____; Address: _____

	FOUNDATION	BASEMENT	1st FLOOR	2nd FLOOR	3rd FLOOR	ROOF
Height						
Ext. Material						
Int. Wall "						
No. of Rooms . . .						
No. of Windows .						
Floor Material . .						
Water Closets . . .						
Lavatories						
Fireplaces						

Remarks: _____
_____
_____

Draw diagram showing street and block on which building is to be erected, size of building and how it is located on lot. Also show distance of walls of structure from front, side and rear lot lines.

State of Michigan   } ss.
County of Marquette }

_____ being duly sworn, deposes and says he has read the foregoing statement by him subscribed, also the specifications therein mentioned and made a part thereof; that he has made careful examination of the plat and plans therein referred to and that he knows the contents of said statement and the same is true; that said specifications and plans are true and contain a correct description of said building lot, structure and proposed work.

_____
Owner or Owner's Agent

Subscribed and sworn to before me this _____ day of _____ 19 ____

_____Notary Public.

My commission expires _____

The foregoing described building has been examined since completion and has been found in all respects to be in compliance with the provisions of the City of Marquette Building Code. A certificate of such compliance is issued this _____ day of _____

_____
Building Inspector

the requirements, a building permit, figure 5-2, is issued. A copy of the permit or a special form representing the permit, figure 5-3, must be posted on the building site before construction begins, and must remain there until the structure is completed and inspected by the local building inspectors. As indicated in figure 5-2, an additional permit must be obtained for the electrical wiring in some particular areas.

No. 5330

BUILDING PERMIT

THE CITY OF MARQUETTE, MICHIGAN

Permission is hereby granted _____

to _____ a building at the following dimensions, materials, cost and value, upon the following premises in the City of Marquette, Michigan, viz:

PREMISES

LOT	BLOCK	ADDITION

Said improvement to consist of _____

Address _____

and be subject to all the ordinances and regulations of said City applicable thereto, and subject to all other permits required therefor.

DIMENSIONS

Ground floor of main building: _____

Ground floor of additions: _____

MATERIALS OF CONSTRUCTION

STORES	BUILDING		ADDITIONS	
	Exterior	Interior	Exterior	Interior
Cellar				
Basement				
First				
Second				
Third				
Roof				

Estimated cost or value of improvements, $_____

Dated, Marquette, Michigan _____ 19___

This permit is partial only. An additional permit must be obtained from the State Electrical Inspector, University Center Bldg., Marquette, Mich. 226-3291 before any electrical wiring is done.

_____
_____
Owner of said premises

Application filed, and permit issued, this _____ day of _____ 19___

_____
Building inspector

Fig. 5-2 Typical Building Permit.

Courtesy of Marquette City Hall, Marquette, Michigan

BUILDING PERMIT

Conforming to Building Code and Zoning Ordinance of the City of Marquette

PERMIT NO. _____

Has been issued to

_____

OWNER

to perform the work noted here on a building located upon the following premises in the City of Marquette.

Lot _____ **Block** _____ **Addition** _____

Street Address _____

Date _____   _____

City Building Inspector

Permit issued for:

☐ **ERECTING**   ☐ **MOVING**

☐ **ALTERING**   ☐ **DEMOLISHING**

☐ **REPAIRING**   ☐ **FENCE**

THIS CARD IS TO BE DISPLAYED SO THAT IT CAN
BE SEEN FROM THE STREET

Fig. 5-3 Copy of building permit which is posted at the construction side.

Courtesy of Marquette City Hall, Marquette, Michigan

INSPECTIONS

Each phase of construction must be inspected and approved. In some areas, an inspection card is posted at the building site before construction begins in addition to the permit. In other areas, the inspection card is part of the building permit. The work is inspected as each phase is completed and must be approved by the inspector, shown by his signature. The inspector's signature is required before final approval can be given for occupancy of the building.

APPLICATION

Complete each statement with the correct word or words.

1. All residential structures must meet minimum standards as specified by _____.

2. Building codes cover four major stages or phases of construction, including _____.

3. The contractor who erects a foundation must consult the local building codes to ensure that _____ are poured below the frost line.

4. The minimum distance between the _____ and the top of the foundation wall is specified in most building codes.

5. Building codes in hurricane areas regulate _____ methods.

6. To obtain a building permit, the builder must file a (an) _____, accompanied by a complete set of _____ and _____.

7. A (an) _____ must be posted at all building sites before construction can begin.

8. A building inspector's signature on a (an) _____ indicates that the work has been inspected and meets the required standards.

9. Because it is so difficult to keep local building codes updated, some organizations provide current _____, which have been adopted by many communities.

10. The FHA specifies that the floor level of any habitable room cannot be more than _____ inches below the grade level of the exterior wall.

Unit 6   The Building Site

OBJECTIVES

After studying this unit, the student will be able to

- identify items which must be considered when choosing a building site.
- solve specific problems created by building site limitations.
- list zoning restrictions for residential areas.

Building sites must be carefully selected by the builder or prospective owner. Physical limitations may alter construction procedures. Both site limitations and zoning regulations may require expensive construction procedures or structural restrictions. The builder or contractor who is responsible for the concrete form construction must consider the limitations of the building site before a foundation or other construction can begin.

PHYSICAL RESTRICTIONS

Soil Limitations

The physical limitations of a building site come from two basic sources, the soil and the topography of the building site.

As previously mentioned, a professional analysis should be made of the soil at the proposed building site before a final decision concerning the construction is made. The soil analysis determines the permeability of the soil, the water absorption rate, the approximate bearing strength of the soil, whether the soil is in a disturbed or undisturbed state, the depth of the various layers *(strata),* and the type of soil. The soils engineer who performs the analysis is able to make a professional recommendation on the value or rating of the soil as a foundation base material.

The soil analysis and the recommendations of the soils engineer indicate where precautions must be taken to provide a stable foundation base which is able to support the structural weight of the building.

For example, the footings must be placed more deeply than normal if a clay stratum exists at the frost line. The building code for every community specifies how deeply a footing must be poured to be placed below the frost line depth; however, if a clay stratum exists at the frost line, the footing must be poured more deeply than normal to prevent heaving. This is necessary because clay stratum can be particularly elastic. Water drains along the top layer of the clay where it is absorbed, thereby softening the clay and lowering the structural strength of the soil. In colder climates, moisture freezes in the clay stratum, causing heaving of the structure. Consequently, footings should be poured below the clay stratum even though they will be placed more deeply than the footing requirements specified by the local building code in that particular area.

The classification of the soil and its moisture absorption rate also provides the information needed to determine the precautions which must be taken when installing the drainage system. For example, if the soil has a high clay content, loose, porous gravel backfill should extend to within 6 to 8 inches of the grade line, figure 6-1. Some areas with a high water table are not suitable for basement construction particularly if they contain clayey soil. However, in some areas with a high water table, a basement can be constructed by observing extreme caution when waterproofing and installing the drainage system. These procedures may increase the total cost of the structure so much that in some cases construction is not feasible.

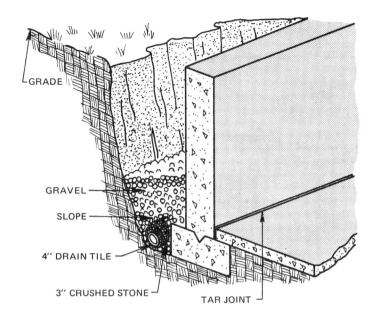

Fig. 6-1 Backfill in clayey soil.

A soil analysis also determines whether the soil is undistributed soil or fill. A different procedure should be followed if the foundation is to be erected on fill soil. If the building site has been a fill area within the past ten years, test holes should be drilled to determine the depth of the fill. If the building site is a fill area, the footings should be poured on a series of piers which are resting on original soil.

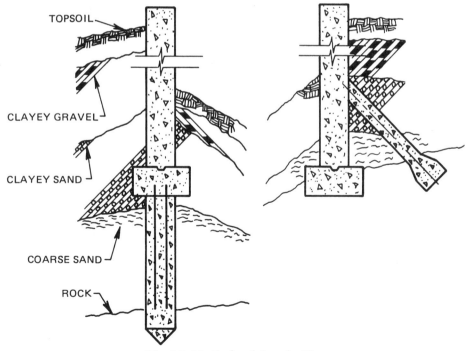

Fig. 6-2 Vertical and Angular Piers.

The piers used may be of two basic types, vertical or angular, figure 6-2, page 33. The *vertical pier* is a concrete pier which has been poured directly into vertical holes which have been drilled underneath the footing. The *angular pier* is poured into a slope at an angle and serves as an anchor for walls. The angular pier is used primarily on sloping sites. Both types of piers may be either cased or poured directly into the drilled hole. The method used in pouring is determined by the porousness (or *porosity*) of the soil. If the soil is porous, a metal or composition casing should be used to prevent the walls from caving in as the concrete is poured in the hole. All piers should be reinforced as required by local building codes.

Topographical Limitations

The topography of a building site may place limitations on the construction of a residence. For example, the slope of a site may drop so severely that it would be economically impractical to construct a residence on the site. If a residence is constructed on a site with an extremely steep slope, precautions such as retaining walls must be taken to create a stable area surrounding the building site, figure 6-3.

The reinforced concrete retaining wall is placed across the slope in back of the structure. Weep holes are installed about 6 inches from the bottom of the wall to ensure adequate drainage of the area surrounding the structure, figure 6-4. Weep holes are installed by placing 4-inch drain tiles through the wall, which provides an escape route for the water. The retaining sides of weep holes should be filled with gravel to provide better flowage. Many sites can be utilized for residential building by the construction of a retaining wall. In figure 6-5, page 35, the concrete forms are shown from inside the retaining wall. When construction is completed, the visible area will be a driveway to a basement garage of a residence. The concrete form in the center is a tie wall which is used to anchor the rear wall. The footing of the structure will be poured on original soil below the frost line. It will be tied to the retaining wall by reinforcement rods. After the concrete has cured and the forms are removed, the area will be filled with porous material and the driveway area will be surfaced. This procedure ensures an excellent foundation area, but it can be very expensive. The expense is determined by the size of the retaining wall and the area to be filled.

Fig. 6-3 Concrete forms for a retaining wall. This is a measure which must sometimes be taken when there is a severe slope on the building site. Courtesy of Meyer Foundation Company, Incorporated.

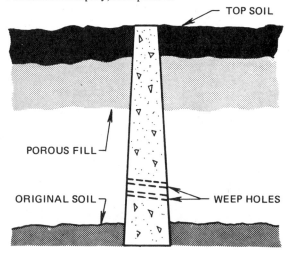

Fig. 6-4 Weep holes in retaining wall.

For a relatively gradual slope, a foundation may be anchored by pouring reinforced concrete piers directly underneath the footing on the lower side of the structure. Another method for utilizing a sloping site is to design a structure which conforms to the slope, figure 6-6.

If a structure has no basement, an economical way to stabilize the foundation on a sloping site is by the use of a stepped footing, figure 6-7. A *stepped footing* is a series of concrete horizontal surfaces which form steps conforming to the contour of the site. As with all footings, stepped footings are always poured below the frost line. Stepped foundation walls may also be poured as an economical measure and to enable the builder to retain the same

Fig. 6-5 Concrete forms with anchor wall forms in place shown from inside the retaining wall.

Courtesy of Meyer Foundation Company, Incorporated.

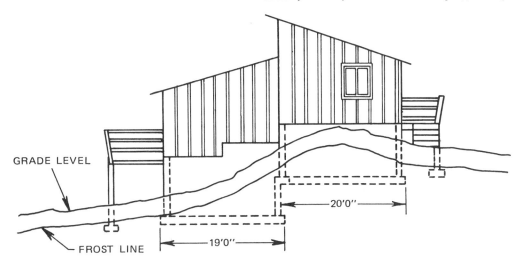

Fig. 6-6 Structure utilizing contour of site. This is a 4-level residence in a contemporary design.

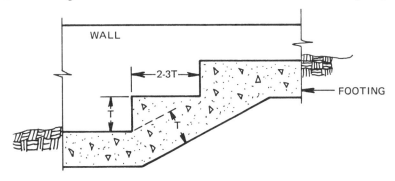

Fig. 6-7 Stepped Footing. Steps normally drop one thickness each level.

approximate distance from the grade line to the wood construction, figure 6-8.

The topography of the building site also has an effect on the drainage of the area. For example, if the lot is sloped toward the center of the site so that a water-holding valley is formed, certain precautions must be taken to provide drainage for the area. The area may be filled or leveled, or a swale may be established. A *swale* is a low, sodded area sloped so that the water drains away from the building site in the proper direction. A drainage system is installed around the foundation to ensure that the foundation area remains dry.

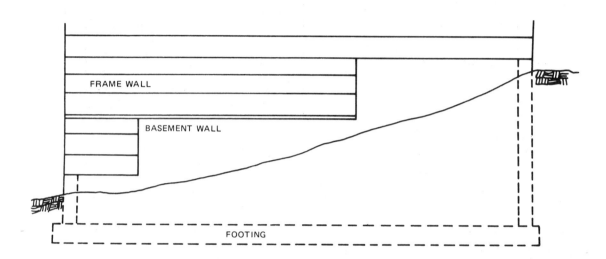

FRAME WALL

BASEMENT WALL

FOOTING

Fig. 6-8 Step foundation wall on sloping site.

ZONING RESTRICTIONS

Zoning restrictions place a limit on the type of structure which can be erected in a particular area. Zoning restrictions are usually classified as residential, commercial, or industrial.

Residential zoning may be subdivided into three categories: single-family residence, multifamily residence, and residential-commercial. A builder or prospective owner should always investigate specific zoning regulations before investing in a building site. Some areas specify that a certain percentage of each section may be developed as commercial property. At times, it may seem that a building could be erected in a specific area but zoning ordinances may prohibit it. For example, a duplex usually cannot be constructed in an area of single-family residences even though the architectural design of the duplex may be compatible with the design of the single-family residence.

Although zoning ordinances, like building codes, vary from community to community, they usually meet Federal Housing Administration (FHA) minimum standards concerning on-site location. Therefore, zoning requirements pertaining to the location of the structure on the building site will be discussed in terms of the minimum standards established by the FHA.

Only a specified area of the building lot can be utilized for building purposes. According to minimum standards established by the FHA, the total space occupied by a single-family residence cannot exceed 30 percent of the lot. For example, if a building lot measures 70 feet x 100 feet, it contains 7,000 square feet; therefore, the residence cannot cover more than 2,100 square feet of the lot. This includes both the house and accessory buildings such as the garage.

Another factor which must be considered is the minimum distance between building lines and property lines. According to the FHA guidelines, the minimum distance from the front or rear building line to the property line is 15 feet. An exception is a rear garage or carport which may be erected within 5 feet of the property line. There must be at least 5 feet from the side building line to the property line, or a total sum of 10 feet, figure 6-9. These requirements apply to a lot that is 70 feet wide or less.

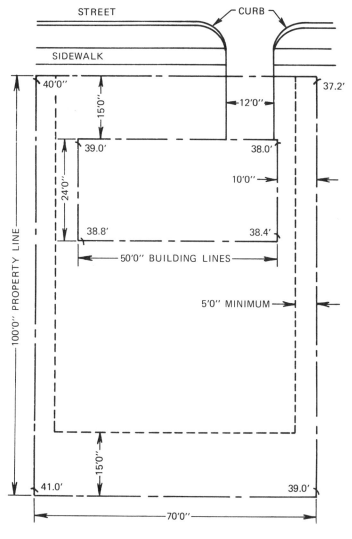

Fig. 6-9 Modified Plot Plan.

If a lot is over 70 feet wide, the total side distance is 15 percent of the total width. For example, for a lot that is 100 feet wide, there must be a total of 15 feet, or a minimum of 7 1/2 feet on each side between the building line and the property line. An exception to this minimum are areas where garages or carports are adjacent to each other. In this case, the minimum FHA standard drops to 3 feet; however, the total of both sides must still meet the 15-percent total or the 10-foot minimum for lots 70 feet wide or less.

Other building site requirements specify that there must be safe entrance and exit access to public streets on the property or, where private, by an easement which is protected by permanent easement rights. The backyard must be accessible without crossing other property. These specifications have been established to prevent an unsightly, crowded community.

Remember that adherence to FHA standards does not exempt a builder from local ordinances. Residential developers may write specific structural restrictions for a development which exceed any part or all of the local requirements. For example, some developments specify that a residence with less than 1,500 square feet of living area cannot be constructed in that specific area. Because of this, it is imperative that local ordinances be consulted before a building site is chosen.

APPLICATION

A.   Select the best answer from the choices offered to complete the statement. Questions 1 through 5 refer to FHA minimum standards.

1.   The total percentage of lot space occupied by a single-family residence cannot exceed

   a. 30 percent.
   b. 20 percent.
   c. 15 percent.
   d. 40 percent.

2.   Minimum distance between front property lines and building lines is

   a. 5 feet.
   b. 20 feet.
   c. 15 feet.
   d. 7 1/2 feet.

3.   If a building lot measures 100 feet x 100 feet, the residence cannot exceed

   a. 3,000 square feet.
   b. 1,500 square feet.
   c. 2,500 square feet.
   d. 4,000 square feet.

4.   If a lot is over 70 feet wide, the total side distance between the building and property lines must be

   a. 10 feet.
   b. 10 percent of the total width.
   c. 3 feet.
   d. 15 percent of the total width.

5.   Even though all FHA minimum standards are met, the builder must also consult

   a. The Uniform Building Code.
   b. local building and zoning ordinances.
   c. Veteran's Administration Housing Standards.
   d. local building trades unions.

6.   Expensive construction procedures or structural restrictions may be caused by site limitations and

   a. careless workmanship.
   b. zoning regulations.
   c. local building codes.
   d. Federal Housing Administration.

7. Footings must be poured more deeply than normal for a specific area when

    a. a clay stratum exists at the frost line.
    b. the average temperature is very cold.
    c. a loam stratum exists at the frost line.
    d. the water table is low.

8. If a soil has a high clay content, loose, porous gravel backfill should extend to

    a. 16 to 18 inches of the grade line.
    b. the grade line.
    c. 12 inches of the grade line.
    d. 6 to 8 inches of the grade line.

9. When a retaining wall is poured across a slope behind a structure, adequate drainage is ensured by the installation of weep holes

    a. about 6 inches from the bottom of the wall.
    b. at the bottom of the wall.
    c. about 6 inches from the top of the wall.
    d. about 12 inches from the bottom of the wall.

10. All the following methods may be used to utilize a sloping site for a foundation except

    a. a stepped footing.
    b. a retaining wall.
    c. an area fill.
    d. reinforced concrete piers under the footing.

B. Complete each statement with the correct word or words.

1. The two basic sources of physical limitations of building sites are the _____ and the _____.

2. If a clay stratum exists at the frost line, the footing must be poured more _____ than usual.

3. A metal or composition casing should be used for pier construction if the soil is _____.

4. A steeply sloped site may be utilized for construction by building a (an) _____.

5. _____ are installed in retaining walls to provide adequate drainage.

6. A foundation may be anchored on a gradual slope by pouring _____ underneath the footing.

7. A (an) _____ is a low, sodded area sloped so that water drains away from the structure.

8. A (an) _____ is a series of concrete horizontal surfaces conforming to the contour of the building site.

9. Residential zoning is usually subdivided into three categories which include _____.

10. According to minimum standards established by the FHA, the total space occupied by a single-family residence cannot exceed _____ percent of the lot.

Unit 7 Surveying

OBJECTIVES

After studying this unit, the student will be able to

- set up and level a builder's level and builder's transit.
- test and adjust a builder's level and builder's transit.
- list the steps involved in determining the difference in elevation between two points.
- measure a horizontal or a vertical angle using a builder's transit.

The first step in locating a structure on a building site is to survey the site. Surveying is done to locate legal property boundaries so that the builder can erect the structure within limits specified by the local building codes. Building codes should always be consulted since requirements vary in different areas. Surveying of property lines is done by a licensed surveyor who locates the boundary lines and places a stake at each corner of the property.

If the building site is located within an urban development which has already been plotted, the *bearings* (compass readings) necessary for the builder to establish the property boundary lines are given on a plot map. In this case, the builder locates and establishes property lines by using a builder's level or a builder's transit.

Regardless of whether property boundaries have been established by a surveyor or from a plot map, the builder should always check local building codes to verify the distance that the structure is to be placed from the street and adjoining property. Erecting a foundation too close to a street or adjoining property causes a great unnecessary expense. For this reason, the figures of the owner or architect should always be verified before the foundation is erected.

SURVEYING INSTRUMENTS

Builders use surveying instruments to lay out property and building lines, lay out foundations, and set up batter boards and concrete forms. The two basic surveying instruments used include the builder's level and the builder's transit.

The *builder's level,* figure 7-1, is designed to level work or to measure angles only in a horizontal plane. A builder's level has the capacity to perform all the necessary operations required by the builder to establish building or property lines.

The *builder's transit,* figure 7-2, page 42, is a more refined instrument with the capacity to make vertical as well as horizontal angular measurements. The builder's

Fig. 7-1 Builder's level.
Courtesy of The L.S. Starrett Company

transit enables the builder to perform all surveying tasks required on residential construction sites.

Setting and Leveling the Instrument*

Setting up and leveling the builder's level and the builder's transit are essentially the same; therefore, instructions are given for the builder's transit only. Refer to figure 7-3, page 43, when following the steps. *Note:* These instructions apply to all builder's levels and transits.

1. Set the tripod base in position.

   ⚝ CAUTION: The legs of the tripod should be set far enough apart to provide a firm, stable base for the instrument.

2. Place the instrument on the tripod. Pick the instrument up by the base, place it on the tripod head, and insert the mounting screw in the threads tightening the mounting screw to the stop shoulder of the base.

3. Attach the plumb bob. The *plumb bob* is a weighted device used to center the instrument over a specific datum point. A *datum* point is a specific point from which measurements are taken. In surveying, it is usually a point established by a surveyor.

4. Visually level and adjust the legs. Tighten the leg wing nuts firmly to stabilize the instrument after leveling the tripod base. The transit can now be moved laterally to bring the plumb bob over a specific point.

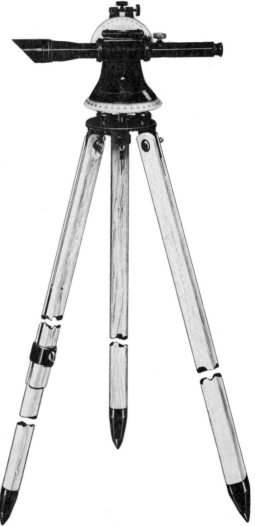

Fig. 7-2 Builder's transit.
Courtesy of The L.S. Starrett Company

5. Level the transit on the tripod base using the four leveling screws.

    A. Set the telescope body directly over two of the leveling screws. To do this, loosen one screw and tighten the other the same amount. This action turns the screws toward each other in the direction in which the leveling bubble must move so that it is centered in the tube.

    B. When the leveling bubble is centered, turn the telescope 90 degrees so that it is directly over the other two leveling screws.

    C. Adjust as before so that the leveling bubble is again centered in the tube. *Note:* To check for accuracy, repeat the process in both positions. If the instrument is in adjustment, the telescope can be turned to any position and the bubble will remain centered.

*The following operating instructions and procedures are adapted from THE STARRETT TRANSIT BOOK, published by the L.S. Starrett Company.

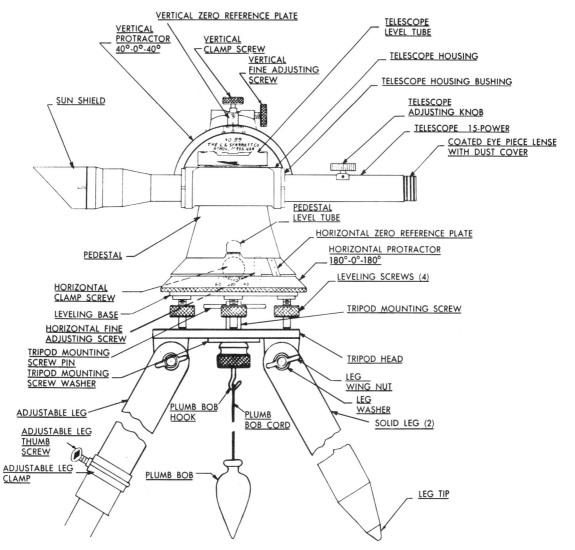

Fig. 7-3 Detailed drawing of transit.
Courtesy of The L.S. Starrett Company

CAUTION: Care should be exercised when leveling the instrument. If the level-ing screws are forced into position, the instrument can be damaged. The level of the instrument should be checked occasionally to ensure that it has not moved out of adjustment. If the bubble is not centered, repeat Step 5, page 42, to re-level the instrument.

Note: Instruments which automatically level themselves are available; however, the price may be prohibitive for some contractors. If an instrument of this type is being used, follow manufacturer's instructions.

Testing and Adjusting the Instrument

The adjustments of the builder's level or transit should always be tested before any critical work is performed. A small amount of time spent in checking the instrument adjustments can prevent costly errors. The following is a relatively quick method used to check the adjustments of a builder's level or transit.

1. Test the instrument to be certain that it is level. If it is not, level the instrument following the procedure described in Step 5, page 42.

2. Test the base level.

    A. Align the telescope with one pair of base leveling screws. Reverse the telescope end for end or 180 degrees.

    B. Check for bubble displacement in the telescope level vial. If there is any bubble displacement, use the level mounting screws to correct only one-half the displacement. Level it again with the base leveling screws and repeat the procedure. Once the telescope can be reversed over the first pair of leveling screws without any displacement, repeat the process with the telescope over the second pair of leveling screws. Once the instrument can be positioned in all four 90-degree positions without bubble displacement, the base level vial is in adjustment and the instrument pedestal is level.

3. Check the telescope level vial by reversing the telescope 180 degrees. At this point, the protractor should be at zero.

4. Check the line of sight when the bubble is in a central position to be certain it is level. *Note:* To check the line of sight, use a surveyor's rod, figure 7-4. The surveyor's rod is 8 feet in length (generally 13 feet extended), with a movable disk known as a *target*.

    A. Choose a reasonably level area of ground. Drive stake A into the ground. Drive a nail into the exact center of the stake.

    B. Set the instrument over the stake with the plumb bob centered on the nail.

    ⚡ CAUTION: Be certain the instrument is level.

    C. Measure the desired distance from stake A and set stake B.

    D. Set stake C on approximately the same line as stake B and the same distance as stake B from stake A. For example, if stake B is

Fig. 7-4 Surveyor's Rod.
Courtesy of The L.S. Starrett Company

set 75 feet from stake A, the distance between stake A and stake C should also be 75 feet. The tops of stakes B and C should be the same level.

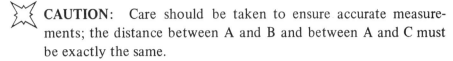 **CAUTION:** Care should be taken to ensure accurate measurements; the distance between A and B and between A and C must be exactly the same.

E. Level the transit over stake A. To do this, use the fine adjustment mechanism to adjust the elevation of the telescope. The telescope level bubble will be approximately centered after the adjustment.

F. With the surveyor's rod set on top of stake B, set the target so that the horizontal cross hair cuts the target exactly in half. The vertical cross hair does not have to be aligned perfectly, but it should be close to the rod.

G. Read and record the target setting.

H. Move the surveyor's rod to stake C. Raise or lower stake C until the rod is in the same position as it was on stake B at the same target setting.

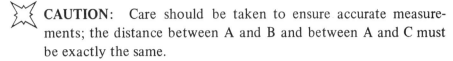 **CAUTION:** The stake must be moved very carefully because the accuracy of the final position determines the degree of accuracy of the test procedure.

I. Set the transit 3 to 4 inches to one side of stake B. Carefully level the base.

J. Set the surveyor's rod on top of stake B and adjust the target until the center is at the same level as the telescope tube center.

K. With the target at the same setting, carry the rod to stake C. At this point, the telescope should be so close that the cross hair can be centered on the target with the fine adjustment mechanism.

L. Adjust the telescope level to center and set the protractor on zero. The instrument should now be in adjustment.

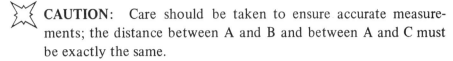 **CAUTION:** To ensure that the instrument is in adjustment, repeat the leveling process and test the cross hair setting.

There is a more accurate method of testing to ensure that the line of sight is level with the telescope level vial. To use this method, stakes A, B, and C should be set as described in the procedure above. Proceed with the following steps to complete the process.

1. Set the transit approximately 20 feet from stake C.

2. Level the base level carefully on the pedestal.

3. Set the telescope so that the level bubble is centered.

4. Place the surveyor's rod on top of stake C and sight on the target. Adjust the target so that the horizontal cross hair is centered on the target.

5. Move the rod to stake B which has been set the same height as stake C (using the procedure described on page 45). Raise or lower the telescope with the fine adjustment mechanism so that the cross hair centers the target.

6. Return to stake C and readjust. Continue this procedure until no further adjustment is needed. Once the telescope is set so that the horizontal cross hair bisects the surveyor's rod when placed on either stake, the telescope should be perfectly horizontal.

7. The telescope bubble level is now centered using the level vial mounting screws. The protractor is set on zero.

The next procedure (if a transit is being used) is to test the vertical movement of the telescope, using the following steps.

1. Erect the instrument in a place where a plumb line is available and level the base.

2. Sight the intersection of the two cross hairs at the top of the plumb line. This is done to move the telescope vertically through a $\pm$ 40-degree angle.

3. Firmly tighten the horizontal clamp screw with the intersection of the cross hair set on top of the plumb line.

4. Lower the telescope so that it is sighted near the bottom of the plumb line. Check to see that the intersection of the cross hair remains on the plumb line. *Note:* If the intersection of the cross hair is not on the plumb line, the instrument is out of adjustment. The vertical motion of the instrument cannot be adjusted in the field; therefore, it must be returned to the factory for adjustment. If the instrument is out of adjustment, it cannot be used for aligning vertical columns or plumbing walls. However, horizontal angles on the same level can still be measured or, if the error is slight, vertical angles can be measured.

DETERMINING DIFFERENCE IN ELEVATION

Between Two Points

Once the builder's level or the builder's transit has been tested and adjusted, it can be used to perform any surveying job that average residential construction requires. If the building site is not level, the builder's level or transit should be used to determine the difference in the ground level where the foundation is being erected.

To determine the difference in the level of two points, the builder's transit should be placed so that both points are visible. If the difference in the elevation of the two points does not exceed 8 feet (the length of the surveyor's rod), the difference in level can be determined from readings taken with the surveyor's rod at each point. The difference in the two readings is the difference in the elevation of the two points.

To determine the difference in elevation, the following procedure should be followed.

1. Set the transit so that the base level and the telescope level bubble are centered.

2. Place the surveyor's rod at the lower point. The rod should always be placed in as vertical a position as possible. *Note:* To ensure accuracy, the distance from the builder's transit to each of the points should be approximately equal. This can be done by pacing off the distance.

3. Set the target to the level of the cross hair and record the readings.

4. Move to the other point and repeat the process.

5. Subtract the second reading from the first. The result is the difference in the elevation of the two points, figure 7-5.

With Multiple Settings

If the distance between the two points is too great, or if the elevation points are not within sight of each other, more than one setting is required to determine the difference in elevation.

1. Select intermediate points which are approximately the same distance apart.

2. Drive stakes at each point and label each point at which a reading is to be taken, such as point 1 and point 2.

3. Take readings at points 1 and 2 following the procedure described above.

4. Move the transit and take readings between points 2 and 3, 3 and 4,

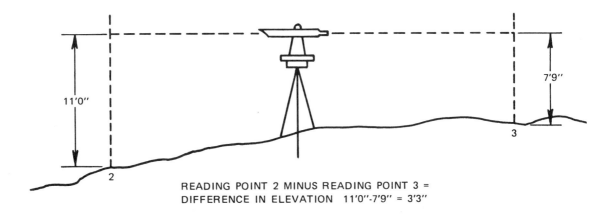

11'0"

7'9"

2

3

READING POINT 2 MINUS READING POINT 3 =
DIFFERENCE IN ELEVATION 11'0"-7'9" = 3'3"

Fig. 7-5 Finding the difference in elevation between two points.

4 and 5, and 5 and 6. Record all readings, figure 7-6. *Note:* The *backsight* reading is the reading taken when measuring upward from the ground to the instrument, or the reading at point 1. The *foresight* reading is the reading taken when measuring from the instrument downward to the ground, or the reading at point 2. When the transit is moved to the second intermediate step, the backsight reading is at point 2. The foresight reading is at point 3.

5. Add the backsights to obtain the total measurement upward from the ground to the instrument.

6. Add the foresight readings to obtain the total measurement downward from the instrument to the ground.

7. The difference between the two totals is the difference in elevation between points 1 and 6. If the sum of the backsights is higher than the sum of the foresights, the last point, or point 6 in the example, is higher than the first point.

CAUTION: To ensure accuracy, be certain that the base is level and that the telescope level bubble is centered. Greater accuracy is obtained if sights no greater than 100 to 200 feet away are measured.

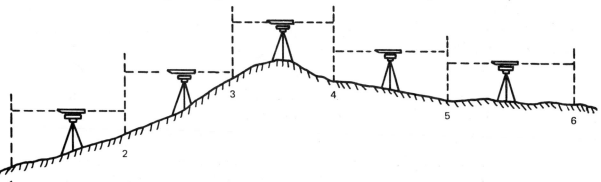

RECORDED DATA FROM READINGS		
POINT	**BACKSIGHTS**	**FORESIGHTS**
1	3' 6"	
2	4' 0"	1' 0"
3	5' 6"	0' 6"
4	3' 0"	6' 6"
5	4' 6"	4' 6"
6		5' 0"
DIFFERENCE IN ELEVATION IS	20' 6" −17' 6" 3' 0"	17' 6"

Fig. 7-6 Finding the difference in elevation between two points by use of multiple settings.

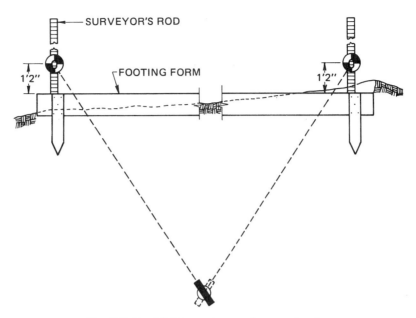

Fig. 7-7 Establishing points at the same level.

Between Points at the Same Level

A builder's level or a builder's transit is used most frequently to establish points at the same level when setting forms for footings and foundation walls, figure 7-7. To establish points at the same level, the following procedure should be followed.

1. Set up the transit and level the base and telescope.

2. Choose a point which is at the required level. Hold the surveyor's rod at that point.

3. Set the target so that the horizontal cross hair bisects it.

4. Record the reading so that it can be checked later to ensure greater accuracy. Maintain the same target reading so that all other points may be set on the same level.

5. Hold the surveyor's rod at each point and raise or lower the rod until the target is bisected by the cross hair.

6. Adjust the concrete form or a stake so that it touches the bottom of the rod.

MEASURING AND LAYING OUT ANGLES

Horizontal Angles

A builder's level or transit is also used to measure and to lay out horizontal angles. Refer to figure 7-8, page 50, while following the steps to measure a horizontal angle.

1. Set the instrument over the *vertex* of the angle (the point at which the two sides meet).

2. Level the base and the telescope.

3. Position the transit using the plumb bob.

4. Move the telescope until the viewer can sight along the first side of the angle. Tighten the clamp screw to hold the telescope in position.

5. Set the protractor ring so that the zero is under the horizontal reference point.

6. Loosen the clamp screw and turn the telescope until the viewer can sight along the second angle.

7. Tighten the clamp screw and read the angle on the protractor at the zero reference.

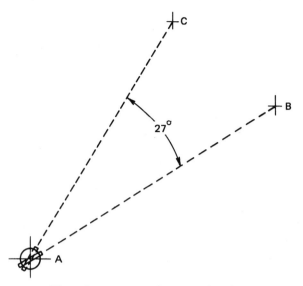

Fig. 7-8 Laying out horizontal angles.

To lay out a horizontal angle, the following procedure is used.

1. Sight in the telescope along the first side of the angle.

2. Tighten the clamp screw and set the protractor on zero.

3. Lay out the second side of the angle by swinging the telescope around until the desired angle is set on the protractor. For accuracy, use the fine adjustment mechanism.

4. Set the stake in line with the vertical cross hair to mark the angle.

Vertical Angles

The measurement of vertical angles cannot be performed with a builder's level; therefore, a builder's transit must be used for this procedure. Refer to figure 7-9, page 51.

1. Set up the transit. Be sure the base and telescope are level.

2. Loosen the vertical protractor screw.

3. Raise or lower the telescope until the horizontal cross hair covers the point of the required vertical angle.

4. Lock the vertical protractor in place after using the fine adjustment mechanism for final positioning.

5. Read and record the angle at the vertical zero reference point.

ESTABLISHING STRAIGHT LINES

The builder's level or transit is also used to establish straight lines.

1. Set up and level the instrument over the initial point of reference.

2. Sight the vertical cross hair on the point at the opposite end of the line.

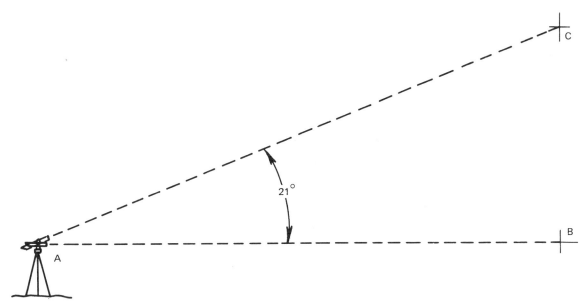

Fig. 7-9 Laying out vertical angles.

3. Tighten the clamp screw to hold the telescope in line.

4. Bring stakes in line with the vertical cross hair so that a straight line is formed.

    CAUTION: Check the instrument frequently for accuracy as the setting can easily be changed by such factors as wind. *Note:* The line can be extended in the opposite direction by zeroing the horizontal protractor scale, releasing the clamp, and rotating the telescope 180 degrees.

The surveying instruments and procedures discussed above should enable the residential contractor to perform any necessary surveying procedures on building sites. These procedures are required when laying out property lines and foundations, setting up batter boards, and setting concrete forms.

APPLICATION

Complete each statement with the correct word or words.

1. When testing the vertical motion of a telescope, the viewer should be able to move the telescope through a (an) _____ angle.

2. The _____ is an instrument designed to measure angles in a horizontal plane only.

3. The _____ is an instrument designed to measure both horizontal and vertical angles.

4. The builder's level or transit should be picked up by the _____ when it is set on the tripod head.

5. The builder's level or transit is leveled by moving two of the _____ in opposite directions.

6. The first step in setting up an instrument for operation is _____ both the base and the telescope.

7. To check the telescope level vial, rotate the telescope _____ degrees.

8. If a vertical adjustment is slightly out of alignment, the instrument must be sent to the factory for repair; however, the instrument can still be used for _____ measurements.

9. The difference in the elevation of two points can be determined from one measuring point if both points are visible and the difference does not exceed _____ feet.

10. When measuring a horizontal angle, the builder's transit is set over the _____ of the angle.

11. _____ is the measurement upward from the ground to the level or transit.

12. _____ is the measurement downward from the level or transit to the ground.

13. When establishing points at the same level, the _____ is raised or lowered until the target is bisected by the cross hair.

14. The _____ is a weight used to position the transit over a specific point.

15. When measuring a horizontal angle, set the _____ so that it is at the zero reference point.

Unit 8 Building Lines

OBJECTIVES

After studying this unit, the student will be able to

- lay out building lines by the 6-8-10 method.
- lay out building lines using a builder's level or builder's transit.
- list the procedures followed to check the accuracy of the building lines.

The first step in the actual foundation construction is locating the building lines. Contractors who are in charge of the concrete work for the foundation usually have this responsibility. They are provided with a plot plan which is usually prepared by a licensed surveyor who has established the property lines.

THE PLOT PLAN

The plot plan is drawn up by a licensed surveyor. *Plot plans* show the datum or reference point, property lines, elevation of the site, grade line (usually curb level), drainage flow direction, utilities easement, and the location of the structure on the site.

When licensed surveyors complete surveys of sites, they locate the reference or datum point and stake the corners of the property. They also list the compass readings and elevations on the plot plan, figure 8-1, page 54. The grade line elevation, contour of the site, drainage flow, and elevation of sewer lines are included to aid in the grading of the site for the final location of the structure. If a building site is steeply contoured, the site may be roughly graded before the building lines are established.

The location of the proposed structure on the site, shown on the plot plan, includes outside dimensions of the structure and its distance from the property lines (known as the *setback*).

In addition to the plot plan, the builder also has blueprints of the structure. The plot plan and blueprints contain all necessary specifications for the foundation work. The plot plan can be checked against the blueprints to ensure that the outside building dimensions are correct. Building ordinances should also be consulted to ensure that the distance between the building lines and property lines meets specifications.

The plot plan and the blueprints provide the builder with the information necessary to lay out building lines. There are two methods of laying out building lines. The more accurate and preferred method is with a builder's level or builder's transit. If these instruments are not available, building lines can be established using a line level and two steel tapes, preferably 100 feet long. If this method is used, measuring should be done with utmost caution and double-checked.

LAYING OUT BUILDING LINES USING THE 6-8-10 METHOD

The 6-8-10 method may be used to lay out and check building lines. If this method is used, caution should be exercised to ensure that building lines are square. All lines should be layed out perpendicular to existing lines.

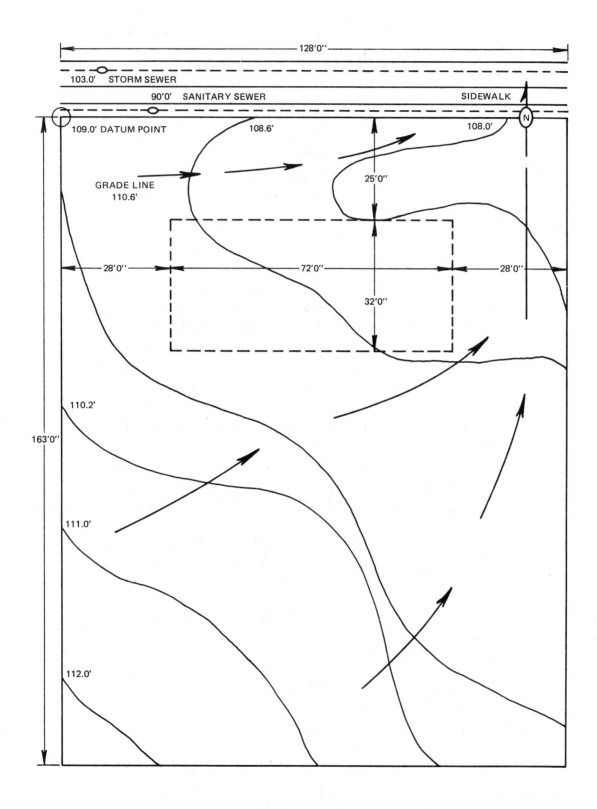

Fig. 8-1 Plot Plan.

1. Locate the datum point and the corner property stakes, established by a licensed surveyor.

2. Establish property lines from which to work by stretching a taut line from boundary stake to boundary stake around the property.

3. Determine setback of the structure from the property lines. Measure and set a stake at each of the two front corners of the building layout. *Note:* The setback distance is obtained from the plot map.

   CAUTION: Local ordinances should always be consulted to ensure that the distance from the property lines to the building lines meets required specifications.

   A. Check the location of the corner stake by measuring both the distance from the front property line and the distance from the side property line. If the corner building stakes are in the proper positions, measurements will agree with the plot map.

4. Establish a base rectangle encompassing the entire structure by measuring along each side and staking the back corners of the house.

5. Check the measurements of the rectangle by measuring two diagonal lines from corner to corner of the rectangle, figure 8-2. If both diagonal measurements are the same, the building lines are correct. *Note:* Use this method each time a square or rectangle is laid out.

6. Use a second check, the 6-8-10 method, each time a corner is established to check the accuracy of the corner angles.

   A. Measure 6 feet from the corner along one side of the building line and stake.

   B. Measure 8 feet from the corner along the other building line and stake.

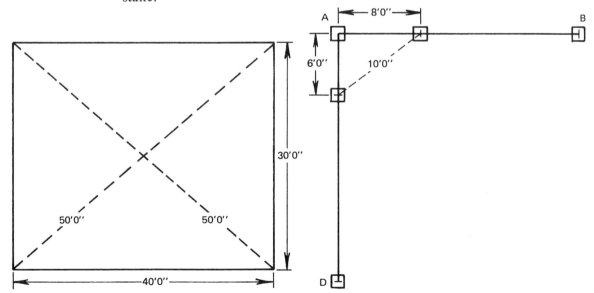

Fig. 8-2   **Checking base rectangle by diagonals.**   Fig. 8-3 **6-8-10 Method.**

C. Form a third leg of the triangle by stretching a taut line from stake to stake. The corner forms a 90-degree or *right* angle if the diagonal between the stakes measures 10 feet across, figure 8-3, page 55. *Note:* Always check each time a corner is established.

6-8-10 METHOD FOR OFFSET BUILDING LINES

1. Locate the datum point and corner property stakes.

2. Establish property lines from which to work by stretching a taut line from boundary stake to boundary stake.

3. Find the location for the corner closest to the datum point (point 1 in figure 8-4, page 57).

    A. Measure the setback along each side of the property lines and stake.

    B. Run a taut line across the property parallel to the front property line. For example, the house in figure 8-4, page 57, is 20 feet from the front property line. The 20 feet is measured along each side; stakes A and B are set with a taut line stretched between the two. *Note:* Drive a nail in the center of each stake to mark the exact point used in the measurement.

    C. Measure the setback from the side property lines at both the front and rear property lines and stake. The stakes are shown as points C and D in figure 8-4, page 57.

    D. Stretch a taut line between the side stakes, (stakes C and D) in figure 8-4, page 57. *Note:* The lines now correspond to the building lines along the front and side of the structure.

    E. Set a layout stake with a nail in the top at point 1 which is the intersection of the two strings marking the outside front corner of the foundation. Be sure to check each corner angle as it is established.

5. Locate the rear corner (point 2 in figure 8-4, page 57).

    A. Obtain the side dimension of the structure from the blueprints or plot plan.

    B. Measure the distance from the front corner (point 1 in figure 8-4, page 57) to the back corner (point 2 in figure 8-4, page 57) and stake.

6. Locate the opposite front corner (point 3 in figure 8-4, page 57).

    A. Measure the setback of the structure from the side property lines and stake (stakes E and F in figure 8-4, page 57).

    B. Stretch a taut line parallel to the side property line from stake E to F. *Note:* This line now corresponds to the side building line.

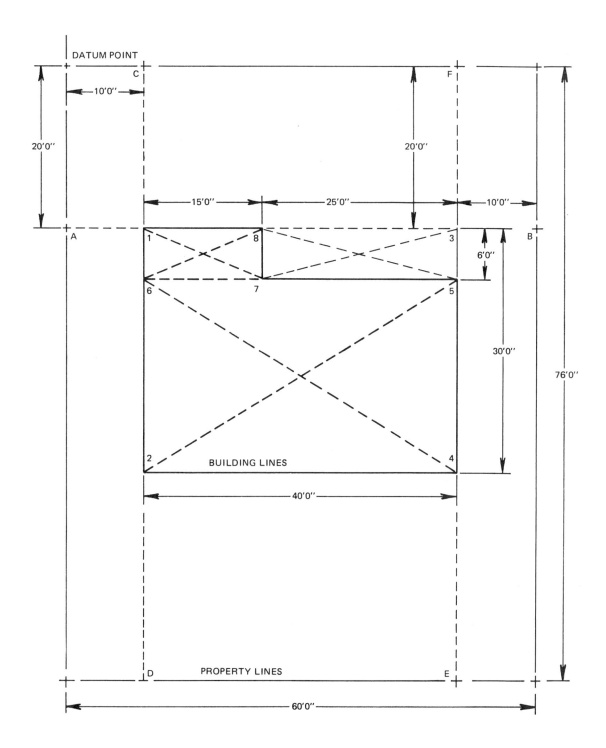

DATUM POINT

10'0"

20'0"

C

F

20'0"

A

15'0"

25'0"

10'0"

B

1

8

3

6'0"

6

7

5

30'0"

76'0"

2

BUILDING LINES

4

40'0"

D

PROPERTY LINES

E

60'0"

Fig. 8-4 Establishing building lines by 6-8-10 Method.

    C.   Set stake 3 at the intersection of the two front lines to mark the front corner of the basic rectangle. *Note:* Stake 3 is used to mark the corner of the basic rectangle, not the corner of the foundation.

7. Locate the opposite rear corner of the foundation (point 4) by measuring the same distance from the intersection of the two lines measured along the opposite side. Set layout stake 4. *Note:* The basic rectangle encompassing the structure is now staked.

8. Check the accuracy of the layout by measuring the diagonals of the basic rectangle.

9. Locate the offset corner (point 5 in figure 8-4, page 57).

    A.   Obtain the dimensions of the outside structure from the blueprints or plot plan.

    B.   Measure the specified number of feet from the front along the side layout line and set stake 5 at the appropriate place. *Note:* Double-check measurements between points 3 and 5.

10. Locate the offset position on the opposite side.

    A.   Measure the offset distance from the front corner (point 1) along the side to the offset line (point 6).

    B.   Set stake 6 at the indicated position.

    C.   Stretch a taut string along the offset between stakes 5 and 6.

11. Locate the inside corner of the offset (point 7).

    A.   Obtain the dimensions for the front projection from the blueprints or plot plan.

    B.   Measure the specified distance from stake 6 along the offset line and set stake 7.

12. Locate the front corner of the projection by measuring the specified distance from the inside corner of the offset (point 7) to the front building line and set stake 8.

13. Check the layout by measuring diagonals of each rectangle.

14. Secure all building lines to the stakes at grade level.

    CAUTION: Check each corner by the 6-8-10 method to ensure that all corners form a right angle. It is very important that the foundation be square or problems will result throughout every phase of construction.

LAYING OUT LINES WITH THE SURVEYING INSTRUMENT

The preferred method of laying out building lines is with a builder's level or a builder's transit because it is a quicker method and there is less chance of error.

1. Locate the property datum point which has been established by a licensed surveyor.

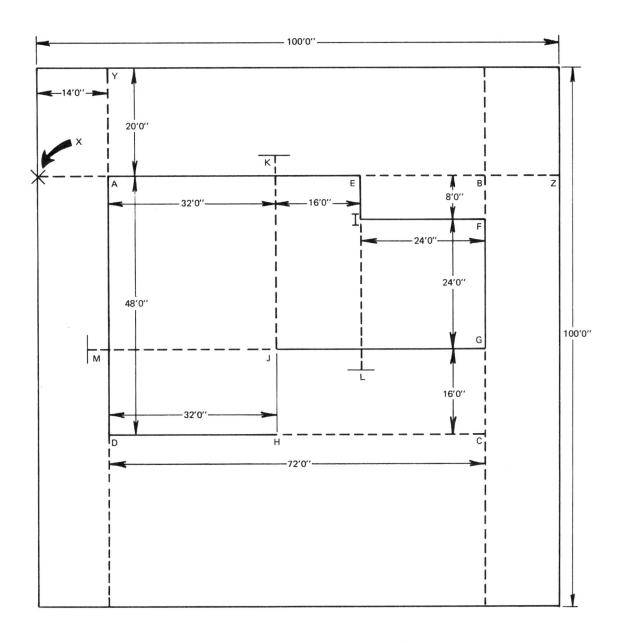

Fig. 8-5 Establishing building lines with builder's transit

2. Locate the front setback of the building line (point X in figure 8-5, page 59).

   A. Set the plumb bob of the transit over the datum point.

   B. Level the instrument base and telescope. Check the adjustments.

   C. Align the instrument along the side property line using the target on the surveyor's rod.

   D. With a steel tape, measure the setback of the front building line and set a stake with a nail in the top at the exact measured distance as illustrated by point X in figure 8-5, page 59. *Note:* All measurements are obtained from the plot plan and blueprints.

   CAUTION: Local ordinances should be checked to ensure that specifications are met.

3. Locate the side setback of the building line (point Y in figure 8-5, page 59).

   A. Set the protractor slip ring on zero and rotate the telescope 90 degrees.

   B. Tighten the horizontal clamp screws and adjust. Use the fine adjustment mechanism.

   C. Align along the front property line, using the target on the surveyor's rod.

   D. Measure the side setback from the datum point along the front property line and set stake Y.

4. Locate the front corner of the outside foundation wall closest to the datum point.

   A. Hook one steel tape over the nail on stake X on the side property line and measure the side setback.

   B. Hook a second steel tape over the nail on stake Y on the front property line and measure the front setback.

   C. Set stake A at the point where the two tapes intersect. This marks the corner of the outside foundation wall. *Note:* Drive a nail in the top of the stake at the exact intersection of the tapes.

5. Locate the front setback on the property line of the other side (point Z in figure 8-5, page 59).

   A. Move the builder's level or builder's transit to the front corner of the outside foundation wall (stake A in figure 8-5, page 59). Center the transit over the stake using the plumb bob.

   B. Level the instrument base and telescope. Check the adjustments.

   C. Align the telescope with stake X on the side property line using the target on the surveyor's rod.

D.   Set the protractor slip ring on zero and rotate the telescope 180 degrees.

E.   Tighten the horizontal clamp screws and adjust. Use the fine adjustment mechanism.

F.   Measure the front setback distance along the side property lines and set stake Z. *Note:* If all measurements are accurate, the end of the tape will meet the center of the surveyor's rod.

As in the 6-8-10 method, a basic rectangle encompassing the entire structure is laid out first and checked by measuring the diagonals. In this way, smaller measurements can be made, decreasing the chance of error. Corners should also be checked as they are laid out by measuring the angle with the builder's transit.

6. Locate the second front corner of the basic rectangle by measuring the side setback from stake Z. Set stake B at this point.

7. Locate the corner of the projection (point E in figure 8-5, page 59).

A.   Read the blueprints or plot plan for the outside dimensions of the projection.

B.   From the outside front corner at stake A, measure the specified width of the projection along the front building line and set stake E for the outside corner of the foundation wall of the projection.

CAUTION: Always use a surveyor's rod to ensure that the stake is aligned.

8. Locate the rear outside corner (point D in figure 8-5, page 59).

A.   Set the protractor slip ring at zero and rotate the telescope 90 degrees.

B.   Tighten the horizontal clamp screws and adjust. Use the fine adjustment mechanism.

C.   Using blueprint figures, measure the side dimensions of the house from point A to the rear outside corner. Set stake D at the rear outside corner.

9. Locate the last corner of the basic rectangle (point C).

A.   Move the transit to the opposite front corner (stake B). With the plumb bob, center the instrument over the stake.

B.   Level and adjust the instrument.

C.   Using the surveyor's rod, align the transit with the opposite front corner (stake A).

D.   Set the protractor slip ring on zero and rotate the telescope 90 degrees.

E.   Tighten the horizontal clamp and make fine adjustments.

F.   Measure the specified side dimensions of the house from stake B to the rear outside corner of the foundation and set stake C. *Note:* Measure the diagonals of the basic rectangle.

10. Locate the corner of the side projections (points F and G in figure 8-5, page 59).

A.   Using blueprint or plot plan measurements, measure the specified distance from the outside corner of the basic rectangle (stake B) to the side projection and set stake F at the front corner of the projection. *Note:* Align the stake with stake B using a surveyor's rod.

B.   Measure the specified distance of the projection from the front outside corner of the projection at stake F to the rear outside corner of the projection. Set stake G at this point, aligning it with stake B.

11. Locate the corner of the projection at the back of the structure (point H in figure 8-5, page 59).

A.   Stretch a taut line across the rear of the structure from stake D to stake C.

B.   Measure the specified distance from the rear outside corner to the rear corner of the projection and set stake H.

12. Locate the inside projection corner (point I in figure 8-5, page 59).

A.   Move the transit to the front corner of the projection (stake E in figure 8-5, page 59).

B.   Center the instrument with the plumb bob.

C.   Level and adjust the instrument.

D.   Align the instrument with the outside front corner (stake A). Always use the target on the surveyor's rod.

E.   Set the protractor slip ring on zero and rotate the telescope 90 degrees.

F.   Tighten the horizontal clamp screws and adjust, using the fine adjustment mechanism.

G.   Measure the specified distance from the outside projection corner (point E in figure 8-5, page 59). Set stake I at this point.

13. Locate the inside rear projection corner (point J) by measuring the specified distance from stake G. Set stake J.
    Note: After the building layout is completed, check the accuracy of the layout by measuring all diagonals. Check each corner with the builder's level or transit to ensure that they measure 90 degrees.

BUILDING LAYOUT FOR BATTER BOARDS

If batter boards are to be used, a stake must be set across from each offset building line.

1. With the transit positioned over the front projection corner (point E in figure 8-5, page 59), align it with the front outside corner (point A).
2. Measure the specified distance to establish the location for the batter board opposite the rear offset (point J). Set layout stake K at this point.
3. Move the transit to point G in figure 8-5, page 59.
4. Set up, level, and adjust the instrument.
5. Align it with stake B, using a surveyor's rod.
6. Set the protractor slip ring at zero and rotate the telescope 90 degrees.
7. Locate the position for the batter board opposite the front offset by measuring the specified distance from stake G and set stake L.
8. To set the stake for the batter board opposite the rear offset corner, measure the distance of the offset from the rear outside corner and set stake M.

ESTABLISHING THE GRADE LINE LEVEL

1. Set the builder's level or builder's transit in the center of the layout.
2. Level and adjust the instrument.
3. Align the instrument with the grade line mark on the datum point. Set the target on the surveyor's rod at the grade line mark.
4. Align the instrument with each layout stake.
5. Using the target on the surveyor's rod, transfer the grade line to each stake.

Specific precautions should be observed when using a builder's level or transit to lay out building lines.

- Always check to be sure that the instrument is level.
- Use a surveyor's rod to accurately align one point with another given point.
- After rotating the telescope, always tighten the horizontal clamp screws and adjust with the fine adjustment mechanism. This ensures that the angle degree is correctly measured.

APPLICATION

A. Select the best answer from the choices offered to complete the statement.

1. The diagonal of the right triangle created by the 6-8-10 method measures
   a. 6 feet.
   b. 8 feet.
   c. 10 feet.
   d. 12 feet.

2. To accurately align the builder's level or transit with a given point, always use a (an)

   a. surveyor's rod.
   b. datum point.
   c. plumb bob.
   d. stake.

3. When using a builder's transit to lay out building lines, the first point to be staked by the foundation contractor is the

   a. datum point.
   b. front setback.
   c. corner closest to the datum point.
   d. rear property line.

4. The datum point is established by a

   a. licensed surveyor.
   b. builder.
   c. contractor.
   d. homeowner.

5. When licensed surveyors establish datum points, they mark the

   a. property setback.
   b. first floor elevation.
   c. basement floor level.
   d. grade line.

6. The first step in laying out building lines is to

   a. establish the property lines.
   b. locate the datum point.
   c. locate the corner closest to the reference point.
   d. determine the setback of the structure.

7. Building line layouts should be checked each time a rectangle or square is formed by measuring the

   a. horizontal offsets.
   b. corners.
   c. building lines.
   d. diagonals.

8. Building lines can be laid out using a line level and two steel tapes, the tapes preferably measuring

   a. 200 feet.
   b. 50 feet.
   c. 100 feet.
   d. 75 feet.

9. The easiest method of transferring the grade line from the datum point to the building stakes is by use of the

   a. builder's transit.
   b. line level.
   c. 6-8-10 method.
   d. carpenter's level and a taut line.

10. The datum point, property lines, elevation, grade line, drainage flow direction, and utilities easement are shown on the

    a. surveyor's map.
    b. blueprints.
    c. plot plan.
    d. builder's plot.

B. Complete each statement with the correct word or words.

1. All measurements or dimensions necessary for laying out building lines can be obtained from the _____ and _____.

2. The fastest and most accurate method of laying out building lines is with a (an) _____ or a (an) _____.

3. Caution must be exercised to ensure that corners of structures are _____.

4. The first step in laying out building lines is to locate the _____.

5. If building lines are accurately laid out, the _____ across each square or rectangle should measure exactly the same.

6. To check corner angles, measure from the corner _____ feet along one side and _____ feet from the corner along the second side. If the corner is laid out at a right angle, the diagonal will measure _____ feet.

7. The exact center of each stake used in a building layout is marked by a (an) _____.

8. The first step in setting up a builder's level or transit is to _____ and _____ the instrument.

9. Once a basic rectangle is established and checked by measurement of the diagonals, _____ measurements can be made for offsets. This reduces the chance of error in the entire structure.

10. Each time a stake is set, _____ the stake with an established reference point.

Unit 9   Batter Boards and Foundation Excavation

OBJECTIVES

After studying this unit, the student will be able to

- construct a batter board.

- list the procedures followed in erecting batter boards.

- identify factors involved in determining excavation depth.

After the location of the building lines has been established, batter boards are erected. *Batter boards* are temporary reference markers established to retain the location of the building lines while the foundation is being excavated, figure 9-1. Batter boards are erected on each corner at right angles and as a straight ledger at each point where the building line should be retained since building layout stakes are uprooted during excavation, figure 9-2, page 67.

THE CONSTRUCTION AND USE OF BATTER BOARDS

Materials

Batter boards should be erected from good quality straight boards. The stakes should be made of 2-inch x 4-inch boards which are cut to a point on one end, figure 9-3, page 67. Ledger boards should measure either 1 inch x 6 inches or 2 inches x 4 inches, preferably 2 inches x 4 inches. The length of the stakes depends on the contour of the site. All stakes should be long enough so that the batter boards are the same height, preferably to the top of the foundation level for working convenience.

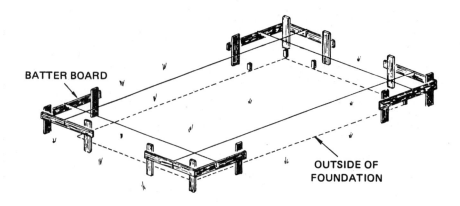

BATTER BOARD

OUTSIDE OF FOUNDATION

Fig. 9-1 Batter Boards

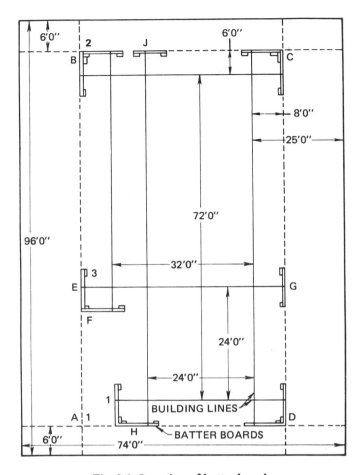

Fig. 9-2 Location of batter boards.

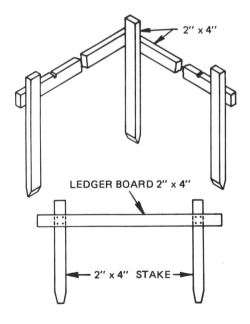

Fig. 9-3 Batter board construction.

Erecting Batter Boards

Batter boards are erected around layout stakes. The distance from the stake depends on the porousness of the soil. For example, in loose sandy soil, batter boards must be set further back because the soil close to the excavation may shift, causing the batter boards to move out of position. In firm soil, batter boards should be set at least 6 feet back from the building layout stake. Two feet of this distance is excavation area.

To erect the batter boards, drive stakes into the ground and nail the ledger boards to the stakes so that the top of the ledger board is level with the top of the foundation. The height of the foundation is determined by the distance that the foundation will extend above the finished grade line. This can be determined from the blueprints.

Establish the position of the building lines on the ledger boards by the use of lines and a plumb bob. Stretch the building lines so that they intersect and cross exactly over the nail on top of the layout stake, figure 9-4, page 69. Tie a plumb bob to the lines so that the exact position can be determined. When the plumb bob is in the correct position, mark the placement of the line on the batter board by a *kerf* (a cut made with a saw), figure 9-5, page 69. The kerf is usually the preferred method of marking building line positions because the lines will not slip out of position when they are being reestablished after the building area has been excavated. The excavation line can also be marked on the batter board by stretching a wire and tying it 2 feet (more if the soil is loose and porous) outside the building line. The markings on the batter boards are retained while excavation is completed.

After the excavation is completed, building lines are reestablished by simply stretching lines across the excavated area and tying them to the batter boards in the saw kerf. The building layout should be checked again at this point to ensure that the layout is square.

Some builders prefer not to use batter boards to retain building lines. These builders roughly stake the foundation area, leaving an allowance for erecting the forms. The area is then excavated. After the excavation is completed, the builder lays out the building lines with the builder's level or builder's transit. If this method is used, it is imperative that surveying instruments are used to minimize errors.

EXCAVATION

After the batter boards are erected, excavation for the foundation can begin. An area at least 2 feet wide should be excavated outside the building lines if the soil is firm. If the soil is loose and sandy, this area should be wider than 2 feet. This space provides a working area for placing forms and the bracing which holds the forms in place, and for the installment of the perimeter drainage system.

The depth of the excavation can usually be obtained from the blueprints. Several factors must be considered when determining the depth of the excavation: the frost line depth, whether or not the structure has a basement, the depth of the basement below the grade line, the height of the foundation above the grade level, the elevation of the site, and the elevation of the storm and sanitary sewers.

If the blueprints are designed by an architect for a specific building site, any problems should already be solved. In this case, the builder simply follows specifications which are

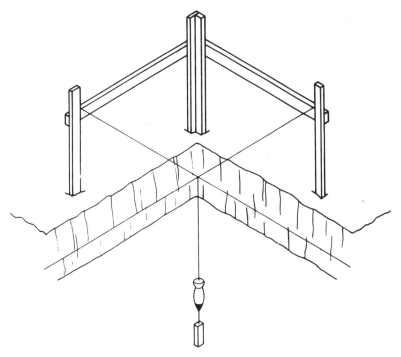

Fig. 9-4 Establishing building lines on ledger boards.

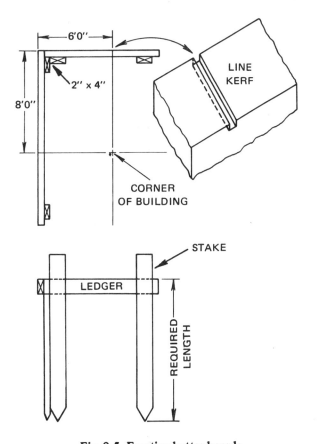

Fig. 9-5 Erecting batter boards.

already established. However, if the structure is not specifically designed for a particular site, the builder may have to solve any problems there are relating to excavation.

The most crucial factor in erecting a foundation is the footing depth. The footing depth is determined by three factors: the frost line depth, the height of the foundation above the finished grade line, and whether or not the structure has a basement or crawl space. If the structure has only a crawl space, there should be little or no excavation; a trench should be excavated to a depth below the frost line for the footing and foundation wall. The frost line depth is crucial, since footings must be placed below it to prevent heaving. In some areas, the footing depth and basement depth are the same, since footings in some areas must be 6 feet deep to be below the frost line, the depth of a typical basement floor.

The height of the foundation above the grade line depends on the design of the house and if the basement is to be finished into a habitable area designed for year-round living. The foundation should always be at least 8 inches above the finished grade line to protect the wooden framework from the soil. If the basement is to be finished into a habitable area, the deepest that the basement floor may be below the finished grade line is 48 inches; therefore, the foundation would extend more than 8 inches above the grade line.

The size of the basement windows must also be considered when determining the height of the foundation. If the house is a bi-level or split-level design, the height of the foundation above the finished grade line is higher than a normal basement foundation height. Therefore, the excavation depth is at the floor level, with an allowance for plumbing space under the floor. Trenches are excavated below the frost line depth for footings.

Sewer elevation is another factor that must be considered when determining the excavation depth. If the structure is equipped with a basement, the preferred procedure is to place the sewer lines under the basement floor so that a drain can be installed in the basement floor. To do this, the main sewer elevation must be approximately 1 foot below the basement floor level. If the main sewer elevation is not below the basement floor, there are two alternatives: do not excavate as deeply for the basement floor and building up the finished grade of the house, or to run the sewer lines through the basement walls.

The sewer elevation also has an effect on the perimeter drainage system. In some areas, the perimeter drainage system can be connected to the storm sewer by permit. However, if the storm sewer elevation is above the drainage system outlet, a dry well must be provided. The dry well area should be excavated at the same time the foundation area is excavated.

The final depth of the excavation is determined by the placement of the footing. If the footing is to be placed on top of the excavation, the excavation will be at the depth of the footings. This is the simplest method if the frost line is not lower than the basement floor. However, if the frost line is below the basement floor level, the excavation is at the basement floor depth, with trenches excavated for the footings.

The depth of the foundation is established at the highest elevation point on the perimeter of the building. After the depth is determined, the area is excavated. It is sometimes necessary to create swales. Swales are formed with excavation soil on the finish grade to provide for the proper drainage of water.

APPLICATION

A. Select the best answers from the choices offered to complete the statement.

1. Batter board stakes are constructed of boards which measure

    a. 2 inches x 4 inches.
    b. 2 inches x 6 inches.
    c. 2 feet x 6 feet.
    d. 1 inch x 6 inches.

2. If the foundation soil is firm, the minimum working space excavated outside the building line is

    a. 5 feet.
    b. 8 feet.
    c. 2 feet.
    d. 18 inches.

3. The most crucial factor in determining foundation depth is the

    a. water table.
    b. grade line.
    c. porousness of the soil.
    d. frost line.

4. Positions of building lines are marked on batter boards by a

    a. chalk mark.
    b. string.
    c. kerf.
    d. paint mark.

5. The minimum space between the top of the foundation and the finished grade line is

    a. 12 inches.
    b. 8 inches.
    c. 6 inches.
    d. 18 inches.

B. Complete each statement with the correct word or words.

1. Batter boards are temporary reference markers established to retain the location of _____ while the foundation is being excavated.

2. Batter boards are erected around the _____ on the construction site.

3. The distance that a batter board is erected from the layout stake is determined by the _____ of the soil.

4. Corner batter boards are erected at _____ to each other.

5. The depth of planned excavation can usually be obtained from the _____ of the project.

6. If a basement area is to be habitable in the finished structure, the maximum depth below the finished grade line that the basement floor can be installed is _____.

7. To install a drain in a basement floor, the main sewer elevation must be approximately _____ below the basement floor level.

8. The final excavation depth of a foundation depends on the placement of the _____.

9. The excavation depth of a foundation should be established at the _____ of the perimeter of the building.

10. After excavation is completed, building lines are reestablished by stretching _____ across the excavated area and tying them to the batter boards.

Unit 10   Leveling the Foundation

OBJECTIVES

After studying this unit, the student will be able to

- construct a level footing form using the builder's level or builder's transit.
- list steps followed when leveling foundation wall forms using the builder's level or builder's transit.

After excavation of the ground is completed, construction of the foundation begins. If the foundation of a structure is not level, problems will be encountered during every phase of construction.

To accurately level a foundation, a builder's level or a builder's transit is used in two basic operations. First, the footing forms are erected and leveled. The concrete footing is then placed. As it is being placed, the concrete is leveled. The forms are removed after the concrete has cured in them for three days. The forms for the foundation walls are then erected on the footing and leveled. If the prebuilt (or monolithic) form is used in which the footing and foundation wall are placed in one operation, the forms are also leveled in one operation.

LEVELING FOOTINGS

To level footings, erect the builder's level or builder's transit in a central position in the excavated area. Level and adjust the instrument. Obtain a reference reading from the grade line mark on the datum point. Determine the difference in the elevation of the top of the footing and the grade mark set on the surveyor's rod, figure 10-1.

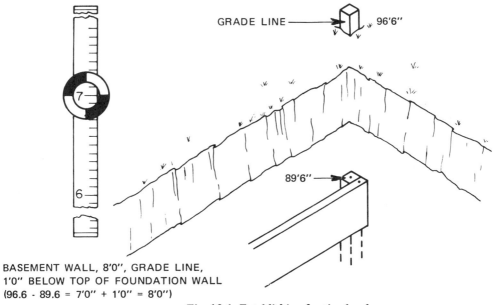

GRADE LINE ⟶ 96'6''

89'6'' ⟶

BASEMENT WALL, 8'0'', GRADE LINE,
1'0'' BELOW TOP OF FOUNDATION WALL
(96.6 - 89.6 = 7'0'' + 1'0'' = 8'0'')

Fig. 10-1 Establishing footing level.

For example, the grade line elevation in figure 10-1, page 73, is 96 feet 6 inches. The basement wall is 8 feet high, with 1 foot extending above grade line; therefore, the top of the footing is 7 feet below grade line, or at an elevation of 89 feet 6 inches. The target on the surveyor's rod is set at 7 feet to assure that the top of all the footing forms are at the same level.

The outside footing forms are first erected for the entire perimeter. The building lines are established at the outside of the foundation walls; therefore, the distance to the outside edge, or the projection of the footing, must be determined.

Under normal building conditions, the projection is one-half the thickness of the footing. For example, if a footing is 8 inches thick, the projection on each side of the foundation wall is 4 inches wide, with a total footing width of 16 inches. The outside edge of the footing is located at the width of the projection outside the building lines. The outside footing stakes are set so that the inside edge of the footing form is located at the width of the projection outside the building lines, figure 10-2. For example, if the projection is 4 inches, the inside of the footing form must be 4 inches from the building line. A stake should be set at each corner of the building by use of a builder's level or builder's transit to establish the correct level. Each stake should be set so that the footing form material can be nailed to the inside of the stake. The top of the stake must be level with the top of the footing. A nail is driven in the center of each corner stake so that a taut line can be stretched between the corner stakes. After the corner stakes have been set at the correct level and the line stretched, all other stakes are set even with the line.

The next step is to position the outside forms. Stakes are set at close intervals so that the footing forms do not bulge when the plastic concrete is placed into the forms. After the stakes have been set, the outside footing forms are positioned by nailing each form to the stake. When the outside forms are in position, they are checked with the builder's level or builder's transit to ensure that they are level.

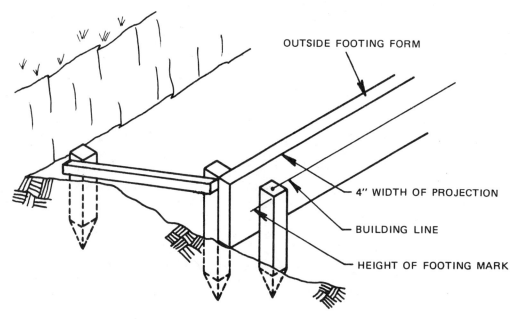

OUTSIDE FOOTING FORM

4" WIDTH OF PROJECTION

BUILDING LINE

HEIGHT OF FOOTING MARK

Fig. 10-2 Locating the outside footing form.

To check the level of the footing forms, set the target on the surveyor's rod at the distance between the grade line elevation and the elevation at the top of the footing. Sight the telescope on the target and lock it in position. Move the surveyor's rod along the top of the footing forms to be sure they are at the same level. Diagonals of each rectangle should also be measured at this point to verify the accuracy of the total layout.

Once the outside forms have been positioned, the location for the inside forms can be established. The inside of the footing forms must equal the total width of the footing. For example, a footing for an 8-inch foundation wall should be 16 inches wide; therefore, the inside forms must be positioned so that the inside of the form is 16 inches away from the inside edge of the outside footing form. The same procedure is followed to erect the inside footing forms. Stakes are set at each corner at the same level as the top of the footing. A taut line is stretched between the stakes and the footing forms are nailed to the inside of the stakes.

The top of the inside footing forms can be checked with a builder's level using the same procedure followed on the outside footing forms. They may also be checked at this point by placing a carpenter's spirit level across the forms, figure 10-3. Caution must be taken to ensure that the footing forms are level to avoid future construction problems. If forms are not level, they must be adjusted until they are level.

LEVELING FOUNDATION WALLS

Setting and leveling foundation walls is a simple procedure if the footing is perfectly level. The building lines are positioned at the outside of the foundation wall. A chalk line

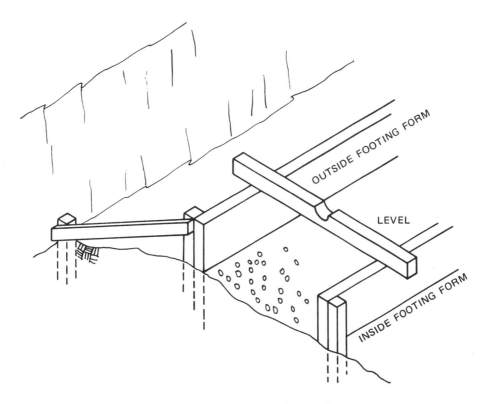

Fig. 10-3 Leveling the inside footing form.

is stretched along the building lines and snapped sharply to establish a reference mark for the foundation walls. A *chalk line* is a line coated with chalk dust which leaves a line mark on the footing when the line is snapped. The foundation forms for the outside walls are aligned with the chalk mark on the footing. Once the outside forms are in position, the inside wall forms are set so that the wall width remains between the forms. If prebuilt concrete forms are used, ties are purchased according to the wall thickness. These ties are available for 8-inch, 10-inch, and 12-inch concrete walls.

After the wall forms are erected at the specified height, the builder's level or builder's transit is used to check the level of the top of the foundation walls. To check the level of the foundation walls, the level or transit is erected in a central position so that all walls can be checked from one position. The instrument is leveled and adjusted. The target on the surveyor's rod is set at the height of the foundation wall. The telescope is sighted on the target of the surveyor's rod, positioned on top of the footing. The target should be level with the top of the foundation wall. The surveyor's rod is moved along the wall and sighted with the telescope at close intervals so that the level of the foundation walls may be checked. Diagonals of the rectangles are measured to ensure accuracy.

If a builder's transit is available, check the foundation wall forms to be sure that they are plumb. To do this, align the cross hair of the transit on the corner of the form. Lock the horizontal clamp screw. Loosen the vertical clamp screw and sight the telescope on the bottom of the form. Move the sight up the corner. If the wall is plumb, the vertical cross hair will be aligned with the corner from bottom to top.

The dimensions of the structure should also be checked to be sure they correspond to the blueprints. This is done by measuring from the inside of the outside wall form on one side to the same position on the other side.

If a builder's level or builder's transit is not available, a 4-foot carpenter's spirit level can be used to check if the wall is plumb by setting it against the side of the foundation wall forms. The carpenter's spirit level can also be used to check the level of the top of the forms by placing the level across the top of the forms. If the foundation wall forms are not level, they must be adjusted until they are level.

Some prebuilt forms are constructed so that the footing and foundation wall are poured in one operation. If this type of form is used, the area where the forms are to be set must be leveled. This is usually accomplished by positioning the form and then trenching underneath the form to lower it, or wedging spacers under the form to raise it until it is level. The height of the wall is again determined and the surveyor's rod set so that the level at the top of the foundation wall forms can be checked. If these steps are followed carefully, the footing and foundation wall should be level.

APPLICATION

Complete each statement with the correct word or words.

1. The preferred method of leveling a foundation is with a (an) _____ or _____.

2. To level footings, the builder's level or transit should be set up in a (an) _____ position in the excavated area.

3. The elevation of the _____ must be determined before foundation forms can be erected on a construction site.

4. _____ footing forms should be erected and leveled first for the entire perimeter of a construction project.

5. The target on a surveyor's rod is set at the difference between the elevation at the top of the footing and the grade line elevation, so that the top of the _____ is set at the same level.

6. After both the outside and inside footing forms are erected, a (an) _____ may be placed across the top of the forms to be sure they are level.

7. Reference marks for foundation wall forms are made by stretching a (an) _____ along the building lines and snapping it sharply.

8. If a builder's transit is available, the corners of a construction project are checked to be sure they are plumb by aligning the _____ with the corner of the foundation wall form, and sighting on the telescope from the bottom to the top of the form.

9. The target on the surveyor's rod is set at the height of the _____ when the wall forms are being leveled.

10. If a prebuilt form is used, the area where the forms are to be set must be _____, which is done by positioning the form and then trenching underneath the form to lower it.

Section 3
Materials in Form Construction

Unit 11　Basic Materials

OBJECTIVES

After studying this unit, the student will be able to

- identify the lumber used in concrete form construction.
- list the sizes of framing lumber.
- compare and contrast various sheathing materials.
- list precautions which must be observed when working with concrete form materials.

After a foundation site has been excavated and building lines established, the concrete forms for the construction project are erected. With current construction procedures, builders or foundation contractors have several options. They may rent or buy prefabricated forms by the square foot, or construct concrete forms on the site. Forms which are constructed on site are being used less frequently by contractors since their construction requires more time and are therefore more expensive. However, some builders still find this method to be economical if the form materials are to be utilized in later construction. This is especially true of the builder who owns a small business and who contracts both the foundation and the general construction work.

LUMBER USED IN CONCRETE FORM CONSTRUCTION

There are two basic types of lumber used in concrete form construction, framing lumber and sheathing materials.

Framing Lumber

Framing lumber is used to construct footing forms. Lumber which measures 2 inches x 4 inches is recommended for footing stakes. The sides of the footing forms are constructed of framing lumber which is 2 inches thick and the width of the footing depth. For example, to construct a footing form for an 8-inch thick footing, pieces of lumber measuring 2 inches x 8 inches are used for the sides.

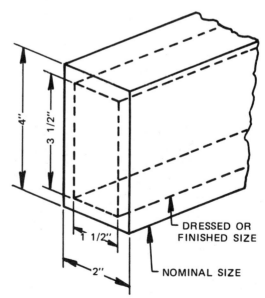

Fig. 11-1 Nominal and finished sizes of dimensioned stock.

Note: Lumber size is always referred to in its nominal size. The *nominal size* of lumber is the size in which the lumber is sold commercially. The actual finished size of the lumber is a fraction smaller than the nominal size, figure 11-1, page 78.

Framing lumber is also used for the basic framework of foundation wall forms which are built on the site, figure 11-2.

Framing lumber which has been used on footing forms may be cleaned and reused. Lumber used for footing forms and framework for foundation wall forms may be utilized as studding, headers, or ceiling joists in general construction.

Framing lumber should be carefully selected. Good quality, straight stock should be chosen to ensure a smooth, straight footing and foundation wall. Caution should be observed when removing the forms so that the lumber is not damaged or the concrete chipped.

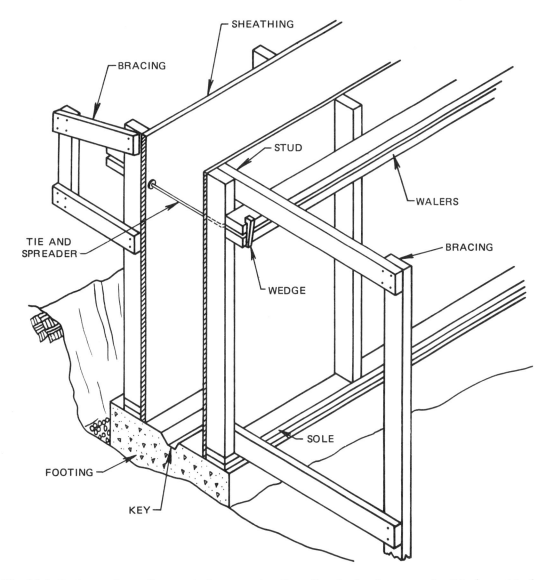

Fig. 11-2 Basic members of concrete form construction. Framing lumber measuring 2 inches x 4 inches is used in the construction of the studs, walers, and braces.

Sheathing

Sheathing is the lumber or prefabricated panels which are attached to the framework. It is used to construct the sides of the concrete forms for foundation walls.

Sheathing for concrete forms must meet two important criteria. The sheathing must be smooth and tightly constructed so that plastic concrete and water can be contained within the forms. The joints between the panels or boards must be so tight that concrete does not leak out. If wet concrete leaks at the joints, a ridge is formed on the face of the concrete. If the sheathing is properly constructed, there should be little or no visible evidence of a joint on the concrete face after the forms are removed.

Plywood is ideal sheathing material because it is manufactured in large, smooth, lightweight sheets which require relatively few joints. It is also easy to handle.

Plywood. Softwood plywood is the most frequently used forming material for residential construction. As shown in figure 11-3, softwood plywood is generally made up of an odd number of *veneers* (plys), or thin sheets of wood glued together with the grain of adjacent veneers at right angles. The grain of the face plys, or faces, runs the length of the sheet. This cross-laminated construction results in a material of superior strength and stiffness.

Plywood has become the generally accepted material for concrete construction for a number of reasons. Since plywood is available in 4-foot x 8-foot sheets or larger, there are fewer joints than other forming materials. The ability to work plywood with ordinary carpentry skills and tools is a distinct advantage. Consequently, various concrete shapes can be achieved at relatively low cost. Thin plywood panels can also be easily bent for use as curved liners or forms. Due to plywood's resistance to splits, nails and form-fastening devices can be much closer to the panel edges. Large plywood panels are lightweight and easy to handle, thereby reducing form construction and shipping cost.

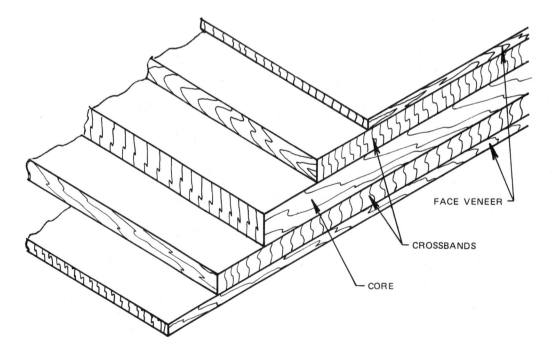

FACE VENEER

CROSSBANDS

CORE

Fig. 11-3 Plywood construction.

Plywood's natural insulating qualities help level out temperature variations and provide more consistent curing conditions. This is an especially important feature since proper curing conditions are essential to quality concrete construction.

Plywood forms are also very durable and can be used several times. In some residential construction, the concrete forms are later incorporated into the finished building as roof or wall sheathing.

Most DFPA grade-trademarked Exterior plywood is acceptable for concrete form construction. Exterior plywood is recommended for concrete form construction due to its greater durability in wet conditions. Interior type may be used, however, if only one or two pours are anticipated.

Any softwood plywood meeting the grade requirements of U.S. Product Standard PS-1 can be stamped with the DFPA grade-trademarks, figure 11-4.

Plyform. While nearly any plywood panel meeting the grade requirements of PS-1 can be used for concrete forms, there is a plywood panel called *Plyform* that is manufactured specifically for concrete forms. Plyform is a proprietary name which applies to concrete forming

Use these symbols when you specify plywood*	Description	Typical Grade-trademarks	VENEER GRADE	
			Faces	Inner Plys
B-B PLYFORM Class I & Class II**	Specifically manufactured for concrete forms. Yields many reuses. Smooth, solid surfaces. Edge-sealed. Mill-oiled unless otherwise specified.	B-B PLYFORM CLASS I EXTERIOR PS 1 66 DFPA TESTED QUALITY 000	B	C
HDO PLYFORM Class I & Class II**	Hard, semi-opaque resin-fiber overlay, heat-fused to panel faces. Smooth surface resists abrasion. Yields up to 200 reuses. Edge-sealed. Light oiling recommended after each pour.	HDO-PLYFORM I- EXT-DFPA-PS I 66	B	C Plugged
STRUCTURAL I Plyform	Especially designed for engineered applications. Contains all Group I species. Stronger and stiffer than Plyform Class I and II. Especially recommended for high pressures where face grain is parallel to supports. Also available with HD Overlay.	STRUCTURAL I B-B PLYFORM CLASS I EXTERIOR PS 1 66 DFPA TESTED QUALITY 000	B	C or C Plugged

* Commonly available in 5/8" and 3/4" panel thicknesses (4' x 8' size).
** Check dealer for availability in your area.

Special Panels

Special Overlays, proprietary panels and MDO plywood specifically designed for concrete forming. Panels produce a smooth uniform concrete surface. Generally mill treated with form release agent. Check with manufacturer for design specifications, proper use, and surface treatment recommendations for greatest number of uses. Check dealer for availability in your area.

Fig. 11-4 Grades and uses of plywood in Concrete Form Construction.
Courtesy of The American Plywood Association

material produced by member mills of the American Plywood Association. Plyform can be manufactured in two Classes, with Class I having the greater strength and stiffness.

Plyform panels are Exterior type panels with B-grade faces. The B grade indicates the face veneer has a solid, smooth surface. Repair plugs and tight knots may be present but the face veneer will be smooth. Plyform is sanded on both sides, then edge-sealed and, unless otherwise specified, oiled at the mill. Face oiling reduces moisture penetration and also acts as a release agent for the first use.

Plyform can also be manufactured with a High Density overlay surface on both faces of a standard sheet of Plyform. The surface veneers are overlaid with a plastic resin material which creates a hard, smooth surface that is moisture and chemical resistant. HDO Plyform can quickly and easily be released from concrete and requires a minimum application of release agent. HDO Plyform needs no initial release agent, but wiping with an oil rag before each pour will make stripping easier. The High Density overlay surface also gives the Plyform a longer life, and with reasonable care, it will normally produce 50 reuses.

If the Plyform is not purchased with the HDO surface, it must be oiled or covered with a release agent before it is to be used so the concrete does not adhere to the surface of the Plyform. The initial oiling can be done at the mill or on the construction site. Some builders prefer to apply the release agent at the construction site so that it will be a fresh application. Often, when the initial oiling is done at the mill, it dries somewhat before the forms are used.

PLYFORM CLASS I

Face grain across supports

Support Spacing	PLYWOOD THICKNESS					
	1/2"	5/8"	3/4"	7/8"	1"	1 1/8"
4"	3190	4070	5010	5150	5590	6220
8"	1030	1370	1740	1980	2150	2390
12"	450	610	770	990	1240	1450
16"	190	290	400	540	700	820
20"	100	150	220	300	400	480
24"			130	180	250	310
32"					110	140
36"						100

PLYFORM CLASS II

Face grain across supports

Support Spacing	PLYWOOD THICKNESS					
	1/2"	5/8"	3/4"	7/8"	1"	1 1/8"
4"	2990	3870	4780	4780	5140	5720
8"	750	990	1260	1630	1980	2200
12"	330	440	560	730	920	1080
16"	160	240	310	410	520	610
20"		130	180	250	330	390
24"			110	150	210	260
32"					100	120

PLYFORM CLASS I

Face grain parallel to supports

Support Spacing	PLYWOOD THICKNESS					
	1/2"	5/8"	3/4"	7/8"	1"	1 1/8"
4"	1550	2250	2780	3740	4460	5280
8"	550	870	1070	1440	1710	2030
12"	160	380	660	890	1060	1260
16"		160	330	520	770	910
20"			170	270	420	570
24"			120	200	300	390

Plywood continuous across two or more spans.

PLYFORM CLASS II

Face grain parallel to supports

Support Spacing	PLYWOOD THICKNESS					
	1/2"	5/8"	3/4"	7/8"	1"	1 1/8"
4"	1540	2240	2780	3740	4450	5270
8"	350	750	1070	1440	1710	2030
12"	100	230	470	700	1020	1250
16"		100	200	320	480	630
20"			100	170	260	350
24"				120	190	250

(a) Plywood continuous across two or more spans.

Fig. 11-5 Allowable pressure (psf) of Plyform, Class I and II. (Variance in size limited to 1/360th of span.)
Courtesy of the American Plywood Association

Special plywood panels, which have textured or patterned surfaces, are also available for different surface finishes. Since textured plywood is available in a variety of patterns and wood species, it is impossible to give exact factors for strength and stiffness reductions due to the texturing. For approximately equivalent strength and stiffness, specify the desired grade in Group 1 or Group 2 species and determine the thickness assuming Plyform Class II. When 3/8″ textured plywood is used for a form liner, assume that the plywood backing must carry the entire load.

Plyform can be manufactured in various thicknesses, but it is good practice to base designs on 5/8-inch or 3/4-inch Plyform Class I as they are more readily available. Figure 11-5, page 82, shows the allowable concrete pressures corresponding to various combinations of Plyform thickness and span.

APPLICATION

Complete each statement with the correct word or words.

1. The two basic types of materials used in concrete form construction are _____ and _____.

2. Studding, walers, and braces are constructed of framing lumber which is _____ in size.

3. The commercial size in which lumber is sold is referred to as the _____ _____ size.

4. The footing form for a 10-inch thick footing is constructed of framing lumber _____ in size.

5. Lumber or prefabricated panels attached to concrete form framework is known as _____.

6. If concrete leaks at the joints of a form, a (an) _____ forms on the surface of the concrete.

7. _____ type plywood is generally used for concrete form construction because it is bonded with waterproof glues.

8. Plywood which meets the grade requirement for concrete form construction bears the stamp of the _____.

9. The B Grade on plywood indicates that repair plugs and tight knots may be present but that the _____ is smooth.

10. Plywood which is used as sheathing material for concrete form construction must be treated with a _____ so that the concrete does not adhere to the surface of the plywood.

11. Plywood specifically manufactured for concrete forms is known as _____.

12. Plywood's natural insulating qualities help resist the effects of _____ and provide more consistent curing conditions.

13. Plyform is manufactured in two classes, with _____ having greater strength and stiffness.

Unit 12   Prefabricated Forms

OBJECTIVES

After studying this unit, the student will be able to

- list the materials used in the construction of prefabricated forms.
- differentiate between face materials used on prefabricated concrete forms.
- compare wooden, metal, and combination metal and wood forms by listing the advantages and disadvantages of each type.

Formerly, forms used in concrete form construction were framed in wood and constructed on the building site. Today, however, prefabricated forms constructed of various materials are predominantly used. Prefabricated forms are constructed in components of various sizes and assembled on the job. If a builder or contractor erects numerous foundations, prefabricated forms save both time and money.

Prefabricated forms are easier and faster to erect than forms built on the site. Each panel of a prefabricated form can be used repeatedly if correct maintenance procedures are followed. The faces of prefabricated forms are smooth with few joints; therefore, the concrete finish is relatively smooth. These forms are easier to remove after the concrete has cured than wooden forms built on site because the prefabricated forms are removed in panel sections. Prefabricated concrete forms are constructed of wood and plywood, steel, aluminum, or in a combination of a metal frame and plywood face.

WOOD FORMS

Prefabricated concrete forms can be constructed in various sizes. Such forms consist of a frame and a smooth sheathing material. The forming system is erected at the building site by placing the panels edge to edge and fastening them together to form a continuous wall of the required size and shape. An example of a prefabricated wood concrete form panel is shown in figure 12-1, page 86.

Straight 2-inch x 4-inch lumber is normally used for the frame or prefabricated wood concrete forms. The frame is faced with an Exterior type plywood, preferably Plyform grade, which is a product made especially for concrete forming. Plyform is Exterior-type and oiled at the mill unless otherwise specified. Plyform can be manufactured in various thicknesses but it is most commonly available in 5/8-inch or 3/4-inch thicknesses and 4-foot x 8-foot panels.

Plyform is also available with a High Density overlaid surface. The surface is overlaid with plastic resin material which creates a hard, smooth surface that is moisture and chemical resistant. With a High Density overlaid surface, the form releases from the concrete with a minimum application of a release agent.

There are various surface finishes available under different names. The surface finish provides for easier release from the concrete and easier cleaning, which, in turn, results in a longer life of the Plyform. High Density overlaid panels are usually available in the same thicknesses as regular Plyform. The standard size is 4-foot x 8-foot, but larger panels are available on special order.

Plywood is also available in various designs and patterns for use as form liners. When nonwood liners are used, plywood is often used as a backing since many of these liners are nonstructural.

METAL FORMS

The wooden frames on prefabricated concrete form panels are easily damaged during the stripping and moving process. Therefore, metal concrete form panels have been designed to provide a sturdier, longer lasting concrete form which can be erected in less time. Prefabricated metal concrete forms are designed in the same fashion as the prefabricated wood panels, with each panel consisting of a metal frame faced with a smooth sheet of metal, figure 12-2.

Originally, all prefabricated metal concrete forms were made of steel. Although steel forms are heavy and difficult to handle, they are still in predominant use for industrial forms because of their superior strength. However, aluminum concrete forms are rapidly replacing steel concrete forms for residential construction because they are lightweight and easier to handle than steel forms.

Another advantage of aluminum concrete forms is the panel size. Aluminum concrete form panels can be made larger than other prefabricated concrete form panels since they are so lightweight. This results in a more efficient operation and a smoother concrete finish because the panels are faster to erect and strip, and have fewer joints and ties than smaller panels.

Prefabricated metal concrete forms are easy to erect and strip because the frame

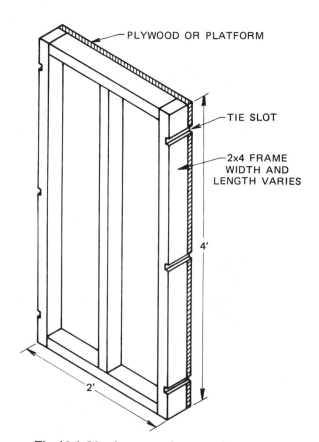

Fig. 12-1 Wood concrete form panel.

Fig. 12-2 Construction worker transporting an aluminum concrete form panel.

Courtesy of Western Forms, Incorporated

on each panel is designed so that the panels can be easily and quickly fastened and unfastened. There are many different concrete forming systems on the market today. Usually, each system has specially designed ties, fasteners, waler brackets, and bracing hardware for a complete forming package. In this way, the builder is provided with materials required to perform the total concrete form construction with minimal cost.

Metal forms provide a smooth surface finish so that little concrete finishing is required after the forms are stripped. They are easily cleaned and maintenance is minimal. Prefabricated metal forms can be used indefinitely if careful maintenance procedures are followed.

- Handle the forms carefully when erecting, stripping, and moving them to prevent surface damage.

- Clean the forms thoroughly after each use.

- Always treat the forms with a release agent before using so that the concrete does not adhere to the forms.

- Repair any damage as soon as it is discovered.

Fig. 12-3 Cross-sectional view of steel-ply panel used in concrete form construction. Notice the method in which the Plyform is attached to the frame.
Courtesy of Symons Corporation

METAL AND WOOD FORMS

Forms having welded-steel or extruded-aluminum frames and plywood facing are the predominant type of prefabricated concrete forms used in residential construction. The metal frames are stronger and less susceptible to damage than wood frames. Plywood sheathing is more economical than metal facings. Plywood sheathing is particularly advantageous for use in these systems as the overall weight of the form can be kept to a minimum.

Metal and wood concrete forms are also economical and practical. The frames are designed so the Plyform faces can readily be replaced when necessary. The frames and fastening hardware can be used indefinitely. Figure 12-3 shows a cross section of a steel-framed panel. Note the method used to attach the Plyform face to the frame.

Plyform is an Exterior type plywood bonded with waterproof glues and has B-grade face veneers. Plyform is edge sealed and oiled at the mill. In addition to having high strength, plywood comes in large sheets which are easily cut to fit various size frames.

Prefabricated metal and wood forms can be purchased or rented as a unit. Some systems are available with a High Density Overlay plywood, fiber glass reinforced plastic overlay plywood, and other special surfaces. All these surfaces are designed to give maximum life and performance to the forms. In some cases, structural overlays provide added strength and stiffness as well as a smooth concrete surface.

When proper maintenance procedures are followed, Plyform can be reused about ten times. In some cases, contractors have reported as many as twenty-five reuses. Overload plywood can be reused many more times.

As with metal forms, each metal and wood forming system is equipped with various sizes of panels, figures 12-4 and 12-5. It is also available with its own hardware. The various sizes of panels and fillers enable the contractor to erect virtually any size or shape wall which might be required in residential construction, including the curved wall. Figure 12-6 shows two standard panels and a filler panel connected by a wedge bolt.

A prefabricated metal and wooden forming system is available which enables the contractor to rapidly erect concrete forms and to pour the footing and foundation wall in one operation. The forms are secured by ties which connect the top and the bottom, figure 12-7, page 90. Concrete placement is a relatively simple procedure because there are no ties or spreaders to impede the flow of concrete. Figure 12-8, page 90, shows the forms in position.

This particular form enables the builder or contractor to erect and strip the forms in minimal time. Ties are easily removed for reuse.

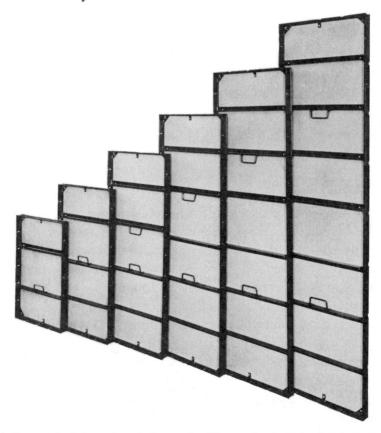

Fig. 12-4 Six standard sizes of steel-ply panels. The standard width of the panels is 2 feet.
Courtesy of Symons Corporation

Fig. 12-5 Various sizes of steel-ply filler panels.
Courtesy of Symons Corporation

Fig. 12-6 Panel construction consisting of steel-ply panels and a filler panel.
Courtesy of Symons Corporation

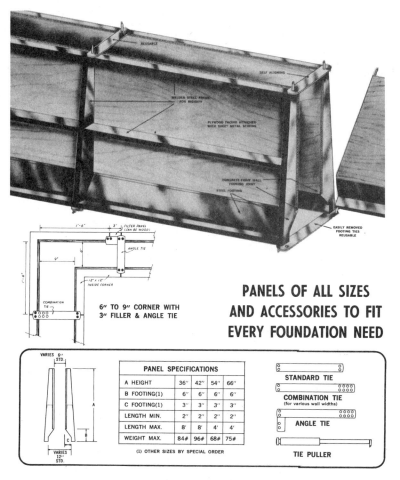

PANELS OF ALL SIZES
AND ACCESSORIES TO FIT
EVERY FOUNDATION NEED

PANEL SPECIFICATIONS				
A HEIGHT	36″	42″	54″	66″
B FOOTING(1)	6″	6″	6″	6″
C FOOTING(1)	3″	3″	3″	3″
LENGTH MIN.	2″	2″	2″	2″
LENGTH MAX.	8′	8′	4′	4′
WEIGHT MAX.	84#	96#	68#	75#

(1) OTHER SIZES BY SPECIAL ORDER

STANDARD TIE

COMBINATION TIE
(for various wall widths)

ANGLE TIE

TIE PULLER

Fig. 12-7 One-piece footing and foundation wall form. Notice the sloped footing. This type of footing meets minimum standards set by the Federal Housing Administration and The Uniform Building Code.

Courtesy of Proctor Products Company, Incorporated

Fig. 12-8 By utilizing various length combinations of the one-piece forming system, any shaped foundation may be formed.

Courtesy of Proctor Products Company, Incorporated

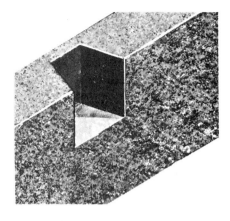

REUSABLE STEEL VENT BUCK FRAMES

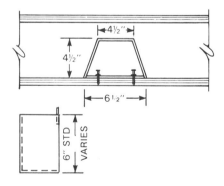

REUSABLE BEAM BLOCKOUTS

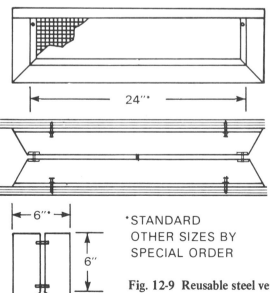

24″*

6″*

6″

*STANDARD
OTHER SIZES BY
SPECIAL ORDER

Fig. 12-9 Reusable steel vent buck frames.
Courtesy of Proctor Products Company, Incorporated

4½″

4½″

6½″

6″ STD

VARIES

Fig. 12-10 Reusable beam blockouts.
Courtesy of Proctor Products Company, Incorporated

Proper Treatment of the System

To obtain the maximum use of the metal and wood concrete forming system, always observe the precautions listed by the manufacturer. It is especially important to handle carefully to prevent surface damage. Clean the plywood surfaces thoroughly after each use and treat the forms with a release agent before reusing. Any damages should be repaired or replaced as soon as possible. Small flaw areas should be sealed with a lead and oil aluminum primer, shellac, or equal. If these steps are followed, plywood should give excellent service as a concrete forming material.

FORM ACCESSORIES

The use of form liners enables the builder to achieve different architectural designs or textures on the face of the concrete. They may be made of plywood, metal, fiber glass, or plastic and offer such designs as simulated brick, random plank, or crushed rock.

Various other prefabricated forms and accessories are available. One innovation in form construction is the reusable steel vent buck frame which accepts either closable vent inserts or a standard screen vent, figure 12-9, page 91. Reusable beam blockouts or beam pockets, figure 12-10, page 91, are another device which may be used so that support beams fit tightly and evenly against the top of the foundation wall. Styrofoam blockouts are also available. Other prefabricated forms include the pier form and the slab form.

The development of the prefabricated concrete form, the liner, and various accessories and hardware has helped to simplify and economize the process involved in concrete form construction.

APPLICATION

Complete each statement with the correct word or words.

1. Prefabricated concrete forms are constructed of _____, _____, or a combination of _____.

2. The frame of wooden concrete forms is constructed of stock _____ in size.

3. Both wooden forms and metal/wooden forms are usually faced with _____.

4. A High Density overlaid surface of Plyform indicates that the surface veneer is overlaid with a (an) _____ material.

5. Facing or sheathing of concrete forms is coated with a (an) _____ to prevent the concrete from adhering to the surface.

6. Aluminum forms are replacing steel forms in residential construction because they are more _____ and therefore easier to handle.

7. The steel frame for metal and wooden forms is designed so that the _____ can easily be removed and replaced.

8. Prefabricated concrete forms are available in various sizes of _____ and _____.

9. Forms which enable the builder to pour the _____ and _____ at one time are now available.

10. The use of _____ enables builders to achieve various architectural designs or textures on the face of concrete.

Unit 13   Commercial Spreaders and Fasteners

OBJECTIVES

After studying this unit, the student will be able to

- state the purpose of a tie assembly.

- differentiate between methods used to fasten tie assemblies in position.

- list the hardware and accessories used in erecting prefabricated forms.

Concrete forms must be secured so that the weight of the plastic concrete being placed does not cause the form to shift. The method of fastening or securing concrete forms in place has evolved from the simple wooden spreader and wire ties to the more sophisticated steel rod with the wedge, clamp or screw-type fastener.

At one time, builders threaded heavy wire across the forms and around the walers. (*Walers* are horizontal members on the outside of forms to which the ties are fastened.) The wire was then twisted with a piece of wood to draw the forms against a wooden *spreader washer* which was placed between the forms to hold them apart. The spreader was the width of the wall thickness. One objection to this method was that the pressure of the wet concrete against the wire caused the wire to cut into the soft wood of the walers, thereby causing the wall to expand to too great a width. Also, wire ties were tedious to install and remove from the forms.

These complications led to the development of preformed ties, which have made the wire ties and wooden spreaders obsolete as a method of securing concrete forms in place.

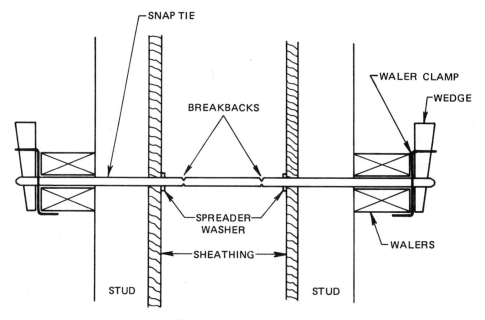

Fig. 13-1 Snap ties.

Modern commercial fasteners are preformed and designed so that the spreader and tie are combined in one unit which is quickly and easily installed and removed.

SNAP TIES

Snap ties, figure 13-1, page 94, are manufactured with a device known as a *breakback* so that the visible section of the tie can easily be broken off after the concrete has cured. The tie is inserted through small holes which have been bored through the sheathing and studding. The spreader washer is set at the correct wall thickness to hold the walls apart. The assembly is tightened on each end by the fastener. After the concrete has cured, the fasteners are removed and the forms are stripped. The outer ends of the rod are broken off at the breakback by use of a special wrench. The hole is then patched with grout or mortar. When the process is completed, the rod is completely enclosed in the concrete wall. The concrete face is then smooth, with little or no evidence of the tie position.

There are ties of various designs available. Normally, each forming system has its own specially designed ties, fasteners, waler brackets, and bracing hardware; however, they usually follow a similar design. Commercial ties are fastened by the wedge, clamp, or screw-type fastener.

The Wedge-Type Fastener

Ties fastened with a wedge-type fastener are formed with a loop or a slot on each end, figure 13-2. The ties are tightened by inserting a metal wedge through the loop or slot until

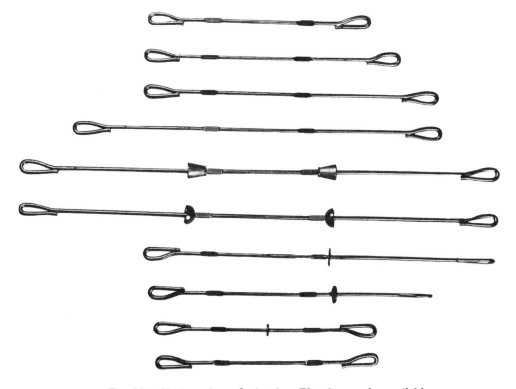

Fig. 13-2 Various sizes of wire ties. Flat ties are also available.
Courtesy of Symons Corporation

the assembly is tightly fastened. There are many wedge-type ties. The standard panel ties shown in figure 13-2, page 95, are made of heavy wire and designed to produce a uniform wall thickness. The ties are manufactured with 1-inch breakbacks in 1/2-inch increments for walls from 4 inches to 48 inches thick. If necessary, special sizes can usually be ordered.

Standard panel ties are manufactured for all types of concrete forms, including those constructed of wood, metal, or a combination of wood and metal. Standard panel ties are made to fit forms which have been adapted to various forming operations encountered in residential construction. One example is the pilaster tie which is made to secure single or double pilaster forms, figure 13-3. A *pilaster* is a section of wall which projects beyond the face of the wall; therefore, the pilaster tie must be designed to fit the pilaster form.

Standard panel ties are also available for forms constructed on the site. These ties are designed with cupped washers or wooden cones which fit between the breakback and the inside face of the form. The breakback for the standard panel tie with wooden cones is determined by the size of the cone, which is normally 1 1/2 inches or 2 inches long. To install this type of tie, the first form wall is erected and the tie rods are inserted through the form. The washers or cones are then positioned for the specified wall thickness. The final

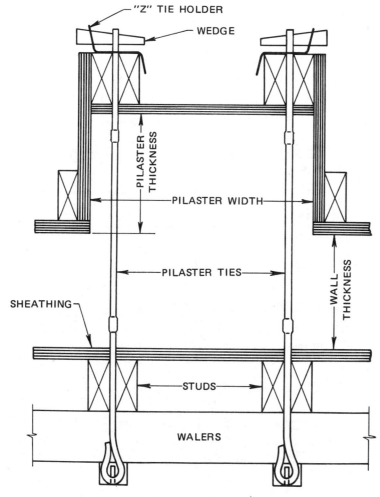

Fig. 13-3 Placement of the pilaster tie.

step is the construction of the second form wall. The washers or cones are designed to serve as spreaders for the concrete forms.

In addition to the standard panel ties which are inserted through the forms, there are base ties and base tie bolts which can be used to secure the top and bottom of the concrete form, figure 13-4. The base tie bolt is positioned vertically underneath or over the form. A tie is placed over the base tie bolt and fastened with a wedge bolt, which is inserted through the slot in the base tie bolt.

The three-way tie, figure 13-5, acts to hold the form in place while also acting as a spreader. The three-way tie is a flat metal tie with holes positioned at spaces indicated by wall thickness. The tie is slipped over pins in the top and the bottom of the form.

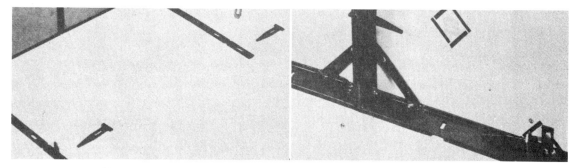

Fig. 13-4 Base tie and base tie bolt used to secure top and bottom concrete forms.
Courtesy of Symons Corporation

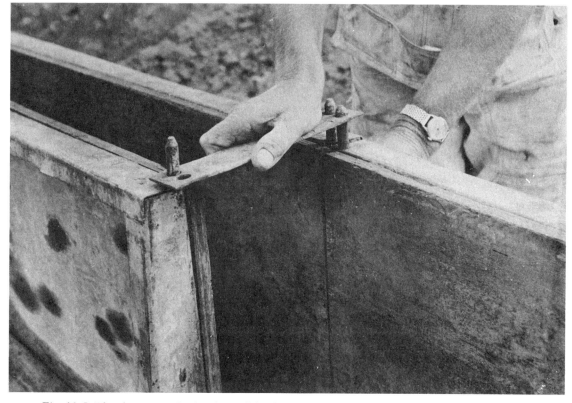

Fig. 13-5 The three-way tie ties the wall both across and end to end, while acting as a spreader.
Courtesy of Proctor Products Company, Incorporated

Because specific sizes of ties must be stocked for the standard panel ties, an adjustable flat tie, figure 13-6, has been designed to lessen the amount of ties which must be stocked to meet job requirements. The adjustable flat tie is constructed of a flat strip of mild steel with a series of slots or holes uniformly spaced across the tie. The ties are tightened by a wedge inserted in the slot at a specific position indicated by the wall size. The adjustable tie is designed for adjustments in 1-inch increments for walls from 4 inches to 16 inches thick.

The breakback is flush with the edge of the outside wall on one end and 1/4 inch below the wall surface on the inside wall. The 1/4-inch breakback for the inside wall enables the inside wall surface to be filled with grout or mortar for a smooth surface finish. The breakback on the outside wall is flush with the wall; therefore, the depression left by the tie rod does not require filling. Since ties are usually below the finished grade line, the tie rods are not visible after the structure is completed.

The Clamp-Type Fastener

Tie assemblies are also secured and tightened by clamps which are simply placed over the end of the tie rod and tightened in position. The assembly can be tightened in position with certain clamps by gently hammering the clamp down until it is secured tightly.

The Screw-Type Fastener

Ties with screw-type fasteners are designed so that the assembly can be tightened with a set screw or a large threaded nut. A threaded tie is designed specifically for forms which are erected against an existing wall. A 2-inch adjustment space is usually provided on the threaded end of the tie.

The standard threaded tie is manufactured in four basic parts: the tie, nut, keeper bolt, and stud anchor, figure 13-7. The stud anchor is used to connect the form to the

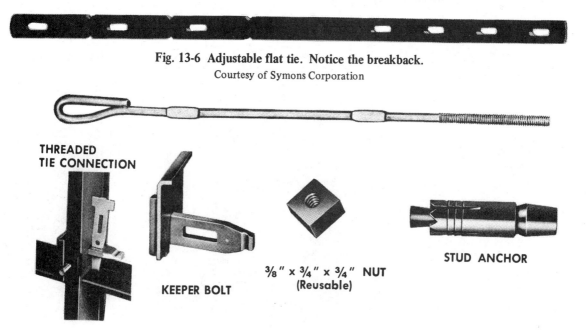

Fig. 13-6 Adjustable flat tie. Notice the breakback.
Courtesy of Symons Corporation

THREADED TIE CONNECTION

KEEPER BOLT

3/8" x 3/4" x 3/4" **NUT** (Reusable)

STUD ANCHOR

Fig. 13-7 Threaded tie with nut, keeper bolt, and stud anchor.
Courtesy of Symons Corporation

existing wall. Holes are drilled in the concrete of the existing wall. The lead anchor is set in place and the tie rod is threaded into the lead anchor. The other end of the tie is inserted through the form and tightened with the nut. The keeper bolt is then positioned to lock the nut in place and secure the form. When the wet concrete for the new wall is poured, the stud anchor and tie provide an anchor to the existing wall.

Another type of threaded tie, the *toggle* tie, is designed for one-sided forming built against either steel or wood sheathing. It is designed to be welded against the existing steel, or attached to wood sheathing by installing the rod through the wood and anchoring it with the toggle, figure 13-8. A wire secures the toggle in place when it is attached to the wood so that any further movement of the form does not dislocate the toggle.

A threaded tie designed for forming of foundation walls consists of two helical coils which are welded to steel rods and fastened by two lag screws, figure 13-9. The coils are designed to fit a specific lag screw size. The lag screws are threaded through each end of the coils, which are manufactured a specified distance apart. In this way, the coils act as spreaders for specified wall thicknesses.

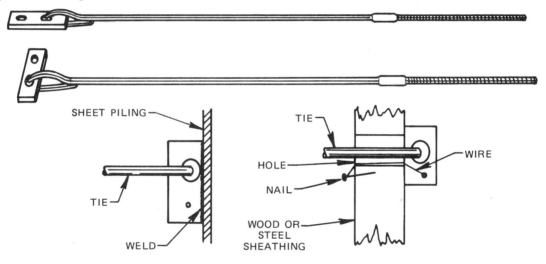

Fig. 13-8 The toggle tie, designed for one-sided forming built against steel or wooden sheathing.
Courtesy of Symons Corporation

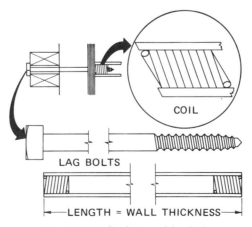

Fig. 13-9 Helical tie and lag bolt.

A reusable threaded tie consists of two outside threaded rods, an inner rod, and a large nut or handle washer for each side, figure 13-10. The outer and inner rods are assembled and inserted through the concrete form. The nut or washer is slipped over the threaded rod on each side until it is within approximately three turns of the waler. The handle is then pressed down over the threads of the rod and tightened. To disassemble, remove the nut or handle washer and unscrew the outer rod from each side. The inside rod remains in the wall. The holes in the wall are filled with grout or mortar for a smooth finish. To re-use the device, order the center insert rods.

HARDWARE

In addition to the ties, other hardware or accessories which may be needed in residential concrete form construction include wedge bolts, waler clamps, waler plates and wedges, and connecting bolts.

The *wedge bolt* is used to connect prefabricated forms and as a fastener for ties, figure 13-11. To connect the prefabricated forms, a wedge bolt is first inserted through a slot in the frame of the form panel. A second wedge bolt is inserted through the slot of the first to hold the frames securely together. The wedge bolt is also used to fasten or secure the ties by simply inserting the wedge bolt through the loop or slot in one end of the tie.

A *waler clamp* is designed for simple waler alignment on prefabricated forms. The clamp slips over the waler, where it hooks to the steel-ply form, figure 13-12. The clamp is then secured by a wedge bolt which, when tightened, aligns the walers.

The *waler plate* and *wedge* connect two walers by use of a waler tie, which is inserted between the two walers and connected to the frame. The plate clamps

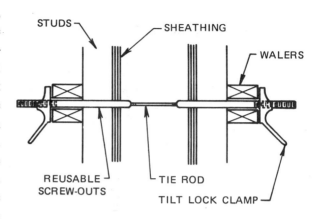

Fig. 13-10 Tilt lock clamp and threaded rod.

Fig. 13-11   Detail of wedge bolt hardware used to connect panels. Notice the dado slot through which the tie feeds.

Courtesy of Symons Corporation

Fig. 13-12 Waler plate and wedge used to connect waler members.

Courtesy of Symons Corporation

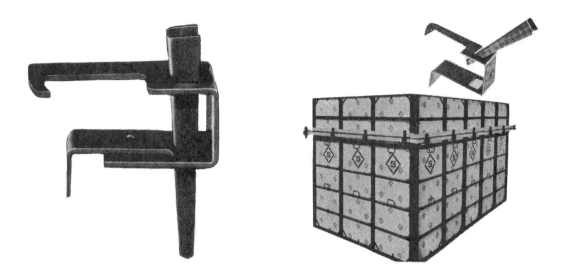

Fig. 13-13 Waler clamp designed to simplify waler alignment on steel-ply forms.
Courtesy of Symons Corporation

over the walers and is tightened by a wedge inserted through the ties, figure 13-13. The waler plate serves a two-fold purpose. It holds the walers in position and provides a buffer which prevents the wedge bolt from cutting into the walers when the plastic concrete is poured into the forms.

A *connecting bolt* is simply a flat bolt with slots used primarily to connect various widths of filler panels to standard panel forms.

APPLICATION

Complete each statement with the correct word or words.

1. Modern commercial fasteners are designed so that the _____ and _____ are combined in one unit.

2. The heavy metal wire used to connect two forms is called a (an) _____.

3. Tie assemblies are fastened by three methods including the _____, _____, and _____.

4. Standard panel ties designed for concrete forms built on the site are manufactured with _____ or _____ to serve as spreaders.

5. A (an) _____ and _____ form an assembly designed to secure the top or bottom of a concrete form.

6. A (an) _____ is designed to act as an adjustable panel tie.

7. A standard threaded tie with a nut, keeper bolt, and stud anchor is designed for use when forms are being erected against a (an) _____.

8. A tie consisting of two helical coils welded to steel rods is fastened with a (an) _____.

9. A (an) _____ is designed to connect prefabricated concrete form panels.

10. The _____ is designed to align walers on prefabricated forms.

Section 4

On-site Construction

Unit 14   Footing Forms

OBJECTIVES

After studying this unit, the student will be able to

- outline the procedure used to construct footing forms.
- list the materials used in building footing forms.
- construct standard footing forms.

After excavation of a site is completed, footing forms are constructed. A *footing* is a wide concrete base on which the foundation walls, chimney, or piers rest. Footings are designed to distribute the structural weight over a larger area, providing a more stable foundation. The size of a specific footing is determined by the structural load and the load-bearing strength of the soil.

Under normal building conditions for residential construction, a standard sized footing is usually sufficient. A standard footing is twice as wide as the foundation wall, with the wall centered on the footing. The footing depth is equal to the foundation wall thickness. For example, foundation walls for frame construction are usually 8 inches thick; therefore, the footing is 16 inches wide and 8 inches deep with a 4-inch projection on each side of the wall. The footing should also always be below the frost line to prevent heaving. Local building codes should always be consulted to determine the minimum footing size and depth for a particular area.

Footing forms for foundation walls are constructed before the footing forms for piers are built. If the foundation wall footings are completed first, it is fairly simple to locate pier positions by measuring from existing stakes, with less chance of error.

FOOTING FORM MATERIALS

Footing form materials are determined by the size and type of footing. Stakes and braces are constructed of 2-inch x 4-inch stock. The sides are constructed of 2-inch stock equal in width to the footing depth. For example, if the footing is 8 inches deep, the sides of the footing form are constructed of 2-inch x 8-inch stock. Always select good, straight stock so that the footings are straight and smooth. Duplex-head nails are preferred for nailing the forms together because they simplify form removal after the concrete has cured.

HOW TO BUILD A FOOTING FORM

1. Reestablish the building lines by first tying taut lines through the kerfs on the batter boards.

2. Stake the outside corners of the foundation wall by use of a plumb bob suspended from the intersection of the building lines. Drive the stakes to the height of the top of the footing and place a nail in the center of the stake as indicated by the plumb bob, figure 14-1.

3. Set up a builder's level or transit in a central position. Check to be sure that the corner foundation stakes are correctly positioned.

   Note: Some builders do not use batter boards; rather, they excavate the building site and then establish the building lines. Regardless of which procedure is followed in establishing building lines, the footing construction procedure follows the same steps once the outside foundation corners have been staked.

4. Tie a taut line to the nails on each corner stake so the building lines are close to the working area.

5. Locate the position of the outside footing stakes by measuring the distance of the projection width plus the thickness of the form material from the corner building stake. Set the outside footing form stake, figure 14-2, page 105. As in the illustration, if the projection is 4 inches and the footing form is constructed of 2-inch x 8-inch stock, measure 6 inches from the corner building line stake. Then, set the outside footing form stake so that the inside edge of the stake is 6 inches

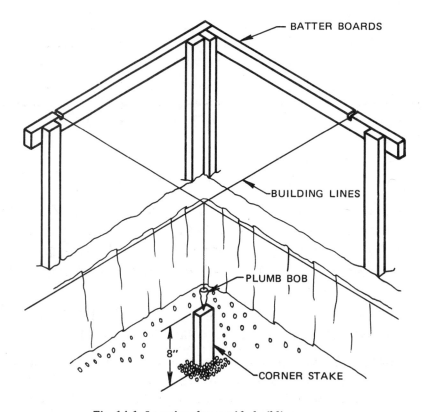

Fig. 14-1 Locating the outside building corner.

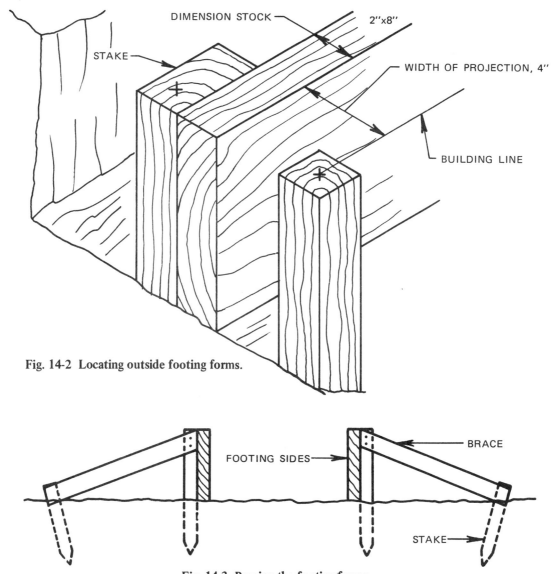

Fig. 14-2 Locating outside footing forms.

Fig. 14-3 Bracing the footing forms.

from the building line. Set the stakes so that they are level with the top of the footing. Set the outside footing stakes at evenly spaced intervals level with the top of the footing. Stakes should be placed at 3-foot to 5-foot intervals. If the soil is loose and porous, the stakes must be braced, figure 14-3.

CAUTION: Stakes must be placed at close intervals so that the weight of the wet concrete does not cause the sides to bulge.

6. Nail the form sides in position on the inside of the stakes. The nails are driven through the stakes and into the sheathing. Duplex-head nails are preferred to simplify form removal after the concrete has cured. Complete the outside forms first. Check to be sure the form is level.

Note: All loose dirt and debris must be removed from the footing area.

7. Construct the inside footing form. To save measuring time and to uniformly set the inside form, cut a spacer the width of the footing. For example, if the footing is 16 inches wide, cut a 16-inch strip of wood. Place one end of the spacer against the outside footing, figure 14-4. Position the inside form by setting the side form board against the other end of the spacer. Drive the stake in place. Nail the form board to the stake.

8. Check the level of all footing forms by the use of a builder's level or transit. Adjust the forms until they are level.

CAUTION: It is imperative that the footings be level; otherwise, adjustments will be required throughout construction.

9. Pour the footing. With modern construction procedures, the wet concrete is delivered to the site in ready-mix trucks which pour the wet

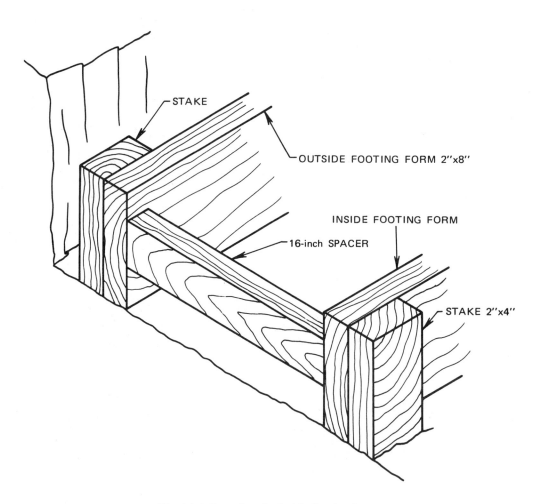

Fig. 14-4 Locating the inside footing form.

concrete through a chute directly into the forms. As the concrete is poured, it is tamped to evenly distribute the aggregates and eliminate air pockets or voids in the concrete. This is done by working a shovel through the wet concrete in a vertical motion or tapping the outside edge of the form with a hammer. The concrete is then leveled flush with the top of the footing forms and smoothed by troweling with a flat, smooth object such as a large metal trowel, a wooden float, or a smooth board. The completed footing is checked with a carpenter's spirit level to be sure that the footing is level, figure 14-5.

Note: Footings must be reinforced in earthquake areas; therefore, building codes in these areas should always be consulted for adequate reinforcement specifications. Certain types of structures, or structures built on soil which is poor in load-bearing capacity, may also require re-

inforced footings. Footings are usually reinforced with two Number 5 reinforcement rods placed horizontally along the length of the footing. There must be a 3-inch layer of concrete around the reinforcement rods. A layer of concrete is placed, the reinforcement rods are installed, and the rest of the footing is placed over and around the reinforcement rods. Rods may also be wired into position with the footing poured at one time.

Fig. 14-5 Checking the levelness of the footing with a carpenter's level. Courtesy of Meyer Foundation Company, Incorporated

10. Tie the foundation wall to the footing to prevent lateral movement of the foundation. There are two methods generally used.

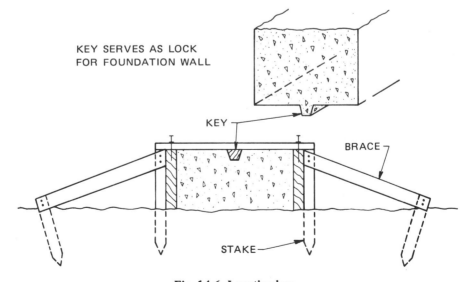

KEY SERVES AS LOCK FOR FOUNDATION WALL

KEY

BRACE

STAKE

Fig. 14-6 Locating key.

A. One method used to tie the footing and foundation wall is the key. A *key* (indentation) is made in the wet concrete by placing a 2-inch x 2-inch board or a 2-inch x 4-inch tapered board along the center of the wet concrete, figure 14-6, page 107. After the concrete has set, the board is removed, leaving an indentation, or key, in the concrete. When the wet concrete of the foundation wall is poured, the key provides a tie between the footing and the wall.

CAUTION: Always oil the board before use so that it can be easily removed after the concrete has cured.

B. One frequently used method of tying the footing and foundation wall is with reinforcement rods. A *reinforcement rod* is a ridged, steel rod which can be purchased in varying lengths. The rods are placed upright in the wet concrete at evenly spaced intervals of 4 feet to 6 feet, figure 14-7. The reinforcement rods become a permanent tie when the wet concrete of the foundation wall is poured around them.

The frost line depth in some areas occurs below the desired level for the basement floor. Footings must be placed below the frost line to prevent heaving; therefore, a trench is first excavated to the required depth. The footing is poured below the frost line and the foundation wall is constructed. The trench is then backfilled and the basement floor is poured at the desired level.

SPECIAL FOOTINGS AND FORMS

Stepped Footings

Stepped footings are designed for sites which are sharply contoured or sloped. Stepped footings prevent the building from sliding toward the lower point, figure 14-8, page 109. Each step of the footing should overlap the other by at least the thickness of the footing. For example, if the footing is 8 inches deep, each step should overlap the other by 8 inches. Each step is strengthened with reinforcement rods placed in the footing. When reinforcement rods are used in this manner, there must be at least 3 inches of concrete around the rod.

Offset Footings

Offset footings, such as chimney or pilaster footings, are required to support

Fig. 14-7 Reinforcing rods positioned in footing.
Courtesy of Meyer Foundation Company, Incorporated

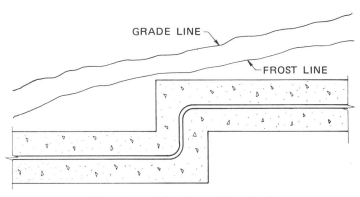

Fig. 14-8 Stepped footing and footing form.

extra weight. Reinforcement rods are installed to support this added weight. If necessary, a two-way reinforcement can be achieved by placing the reinforcement rods at right angles so that a grid is formed. If the chimney or pilaster is located on the outside wall, the footing is poured as part of the wall footing, figure 14-9.

Monolithic Forms

A *monolithic form* is a single unit in which the footing and foundation wall are combined so that they can be poured in one operation, figure 14-10, page 110. Monolithic forms are used predominantly for low foundations. To construct a monolithic form, erect the footing sides and then the wall sides. The walls are held in position by a series of braces. Sheathing is placed over the top of the footing to prevent the wet concrete from sinking at the top and causing a bulge between the footing and the foundation wall.

Fig. 14-9 Offset chimney footing and wall footing poured together.
Courtesy of Meyer Foundation Company, Incorporated

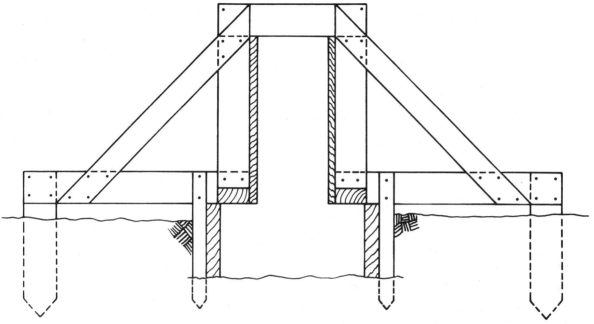

Fig. 14-10 Monolithic form.

APPLICATION

Complete each statement with the correct word or words.

1. Stakes and braces are constructed of stock _____ in size.

2. The boards used on the sides of footings are _____ (greater than, smaller than, equal to) the size of the footing depth.

3. _____ nails are preferred for nailing footing forms together because they simplify form removal.

4. Building lines are reestablished by tying taut lines through the kerfs on the _____.

5. Corner foundation stakes should be level with the top of the _____.

6. If soil is loose and porous, the stakes must be _____.

7. To save measuring time when constructing the inside of the footing form, a (an) _____ the width of the footing is used.

8. To tie a footing and the foundation wall, a (an) _____ is made by placing a 2-inch x 2-inch board or a tapered 2-inch x 4-inch board along the center of the wet concrete footing.

9. _____ are placed in footings when additional strength is needed, such as to support added weight or for use in earthquake areas.

10. A (an) _____ is a single unit form designed so that the footing and foundation wall can be poured in one operation.

Unit 15   On-Site Wall Forms

OBJECTIVES

After studying this unit, the student will be able to

- list and order forming materials.
- determine form design, including plywood size, maximum support spacing, and waler and tie placement.
- construct foundation wall forms.

The residential construction industry is rapidly becoming a specialized trade operated on a contractual basis. Because of this, concrete forms are not usually built in place at the construction site. Prefabricated forms are more economical for a contractor who erects numerous foundations, since they are erected more quickly and easily. However, some builders who are responsible for constructing both the foundation and the structure still build concrete forms on the site and later use the form materials in the construction of the house.

FORM DESIGN

Concrete forms must be strong enough to support the weight of the plastic concrete; otherwise, bulging occurs. Most concrete used in residential foundation work has a density or unit weight of 150 pounds per cubic foot. However, the lateral pressure exerted on concrete forms depends on several factors, including the amount of concrete poured per hour, the temperature, and the amount of consolidation.

The American Plywood Association has developed a series of tables which are used to determine form design, including Plyform thickness maximum support spacing, stud and waler size and placement, and tie placement. To explain the procedures followed in determining form design, the following tables and examples have been adapted from The American Plywood Association booklet, PLYWOOD FOR CONCRETE FORMING.

Example 1. Determine the maximum support spacing for a foundation wall which is 8 feet high and constructed of 5/8-inch Class I Plyform, with

Pour Rate (ft./hr.)	Pressures of Vibrated Concrete (psf) (a), (b), (c)			
	50° F (d)		70° F (d)	
	Columns	Walls	Columns	Walls
1	330	330	280	280
2	510	510	410	410
3	690	690	540	540
4	870	870	660	660
5	1050	1050	790	790
6	1230	1230	920	920
7	1410	1410	1050	1050
8	1590	1470	1180	1090
9	1770	1520	1310	1130
10	1950	1580	1440	1170

Notes: (a) Maximum pressure need not exceed 150h, where h is maximum height of pour:

(b) For non-vibrated concrete, pressures may be reduced 10%.

(c) Based on concrete with density of 150 pcf and 4-in. slump.

(d) See page 27 for concrete pressures at other temperatures.

Fig. 15-1 Concrete pressures for column and wall forms
Courtesy of The American Plywood Association

the face grain across the supports. Assume that the concrete is poured at the rate of 3 feet per hour at a 70-degree temperature.

1. Figure 15-1, page 111, lists the concrete pressures for column and wall forms when poured at various rates and temperatures. This table is based on concrete with the density of 150 pcf. At 150h (150 x 8), the maximum concrete pressure is 1200 psf. However, when concrete of this density is poured at the rate of 3 feet per hour at a 70-degree temperature, the maximum concrete pressure, as indicated by figure 15-1, page 111, is 540 psf.

2. Figure 15-2 lists the allowable pressures on various thicknesses of Class I and Class II Plyform sheets and the maximum support spacing. The plyform in the example is Class I, 5/8 inch thick, and positioned so that the face grain is across the supports. According to the table in figure 15-2, 540 psf falls between 290 psf and 610 psf; therefore, the maximum support spacing for 540 psf on 5/8-inch Class I Plywood with the grain across the supports is 12 inches.

Example 2. Determine the stud, waler, and tie design, using 800 psf as the concrete pressure for a foundation wall which is 8 feet tall with the studs 12 inches on center. *On center* (O.C.) indicates that the measurement is taken from the center of one stud to the center of the next. Assume that the studs are constructed of Douglas fir-larch Number 1, Southern pine Number 1, or the equivalent.

(deflection limited to 1/360th of the span)

PLYFORM CLASS I
Face grain across supports

Support Spacing	PLYWOOD THICKNESS					
	1/2″	5/8″	3/4″	7/8″	1″	1-1/8″
4″	3190	4070	5010	5150	5590	6220
8″	1030	1370	1740	1980	2150	2390
12″	450	610	770	990	1240	1450
16″	190	290	400	540	700	820
20″	100	150	220	300	400	480
24″			130	180	250	310
32″					110	140
36″						100

PLYFORM CLASS II
Face grain across supports

Support Spacing	PLYWOOD THICKNESS					
	1/2″	5/8″	3/4″	7/8″	1″	1-1/8″
4″	2990	3870	4780	4780	5140	5720
8″	750	990	1260	1630	1980	2200
12″	330	440	560	730	920	1080
16″	160	240	310	410	520	610
20″		130	180	250	330	390
24″			110	150	210	260
32″					100	120

PLYFORM CLASS I
Face grain parallel to supports

Support Spacing	PLYWOOD THICKNESS					
	1/2″	5/8″	3/4″	7/8″	1″	1-1/8″
4″	1550	2250	2780	3740	4460	5280
8″	550	870	1070	1440	1710	2030
12″	160	380	660	890	1060	1260
16″		160	330	520	770	910
20″			170	270	420	570
24″			120	200	300	390

PLYFORM CLASS II
Face grain parallel to supports

Support Spacing	PLYWOOD THICKNESS					
	1/2″	5/8″	3/4″	7/8″	1″	1-1/8″
4″	1540	2240	2780	3740	4450	5270
8″	350	750	1070	1440	1710	2030
12″	100	230	470	700	1020	1250
16″		100	200	320	480	630
20″			100	170	260	350
24″				120	190	250

(a) Plywood continuous across two or more spans.

Fig. 15-2 Plyform Class I and II — Allowable pressure (psf)
Courtesy of the American Plywood Association

1. Check the pressure by multiplying the regular density concrete of 150 pcf by the wall height (150 x 8 = 1200 psf). The amount of 800 psf is less than 1200 psf; therefore, 800 psf is considered the maximum pressure.

Equivalent Uniform Load (lb/ft)	Continuous Over 2 or 3 Supports (1 or 2 Spans) Nominal Size								Continuous Over 4 or More Supports (3 or More Spans) Nominal Size							
	2x4	2x6	2x8	2x10	2x12	4x4	4x6	4x8	2x4	2x6	2x8	2x10	2x12	4x4	4x6	4x8
400	40	58	77	98	117	52	82	104	43	65	86	110	133	65	99	122
600	30	47	62	80	97	46	72	94	31	49	64	82	100	56	81	107
800	24	38	50	64	78	42	63	83	25	39	52	66	81	48	70	93
1000	21	33	43	55	67	39	56	74	21	34	44	57	69	41	63	83
1200	19	29	38	49	60	34	51	68	19	30	39	50	61	35	55	73
1400	17	27	35	45	54	30	47	62	17	27	36	46	56	31	49	64
1600	16	25	32	41	50	27	43	56	16	25	33	42	52	28	44	58
1800	15	23	30	39	47	25	39	52	15	24	31	40	48	26	40	53
2000	14	22	29	37	45	23	36	48	14	22	29	38	46	24	37	49
2200	13	21	28	35	43	22	34	45	14	21	28	36	44	22	35	46
2400	13	20	26	34	41	20	32	42	13	20	27	34	42	21	33	44
2600	12	19	26	33	40	19	31	40	13	20	26	33	40	20	31	41
2800	12	19	25	32	38	19	29	38	12	19	25	32	39	19	30	39
3000	12	18	24	31	37	18	28	37	12	19	24	31	38	18	29	38
3200	11	18	23	30	36	17	27	35	12	18	24	30	37	18	28	36
3400	11	17	23	29	36	17	26	34	11	18	23	30	36	17	27	35
3600	11	17	22	29	35	16	25	33	11	17	23	29	35	16	26	34
3800	11	17	22	28	34	16	24	32	11	17	22	29	35	16	25	33
4000	10	16	22	28	34	15	24	31	11	17	22	28	34	15	24	32
4500	10	16	21	27	32	14	22	29	10	16	21	27	33	14	23	30
5000	10	15	20	26	31	13	21	28	10	16	20	26	32	14	22	28

Fig. 15-3 Maximum spans for joists or studs, inches (Douglas Fir-Larch Number 1 or Southern Pine Number 1 (19%). Courtesy of the American Plywood Association.

Equivalent Uniform Load (lb/ft)	Continuous Over 2 or 3 Supports (1 or 2 Spans) Nominal Size									Continuous Over 4 or More Supports (3 or More Spans) Nominal Size								
	2x4	2x6	2x8	3x4	3x6	3x8	4x4	4x6	4x8	2x4	2x6	2x8	3x4	3x6	3x8	4x4	4x6	4x8
1000	35	52	69	44	67	89	49	76	98	36	56	74	52	75	99	60	89	115
1200	30	47	62	41	61	81	46	72	94	31	49	64	47	69	91	56	81	107
1400	27	42	56	39	57	75	44	67	89	28	43	57	41	64	84	52	75	99
1600	24	38	50	36	53	70	42	63	83	25	39	52	37	58	77	48	70	93
1800	22	35	46	33	50	66	40	59	78	23	36	48	34	53	70	44	66	88
2000	21	33	43	30	47	62	39	56	74	21	34	44	31	49	64	41	63	83
2200	20	31	41	28	44	58	36	54	71	20	32	42	29	45	60	38	59	78
2400	19	29	38	26	41	54	34	51	68	19	30	39	27	43	56	35	55	73
2600	18	28	37	25	39	51	32	49	65	18	28	38	26	40	53	33	52	68
2800	17	27	35	23	37	49	30	47	62	17	27	36	24	38	50	31	49	64
3000	16	26	34	22	35	46	29	45	59	17	26	34	23	36	48	29	46	61
3200	16	25	32	21	34	44	27	43	56	16	25	33	22	35	46	28	44	58
3400	15	24	31	21	32	43	26	41	54	15	24	32	21	33	44	27	42	56
3600	15	23	30	20	31	41	25	39	52	15	24	31	20	32	42	26	40	53
3800	14	22	30	19	30	40	24	38	50	15	23	30	20	31	41	25	39	51
4000	14	22	29	19	29	38	23	36	48	14	22	29	19	30	39	24	37	49
4200	14	21	28	18	28	37	22	35	46	14	22	29	18	29	38	23	36	48
4400	13	21	28	17	27	36	22	34	45	14	21	28	18	28	37	22	35	46
4600	13	20	27	17	27	35	21	33	44	13	21	28	17	27	36	22	34	45
4800	13	20	26	17	26	34	20	32	42	13	20	27	17	27	35	21	33	44
5000	13	20	26	16	26	34	20	31	41	13	20	26	17	26	34	20	32	42

*Spans are based on PS-20 lumber sizes. Single member stresses were multiplied by a 1.25 duration-of-load factor for 7-day loads.
Deflection limited to 1/360th of the span with 1/4″ maximum. Spans are center-to-center of the supports.

Fig. 15-4 Maximum spans for double walers, inches (Douglas Fir-Larch Number 1 or Southern Pine Number 1 (19%). Courtesy of The American Plywood Association.

2. To determine the stud design, first determine the load carried by each stud. To do this, multiply the concrete pressure by the stud spacing in feet (800 x 12/12 = 800 pounds per feet). Using 2-inch x 4-inch stock over four or more supports, the studs must be supported at 25-inch intervals O.C., figure 15-3, page 113. This indicates that double walers must be spaced at 25-inch spans, starting 2 inches from the bottom if there is no other bottom support.

3. To determine the waler design, determine the load on the walers by multiplying the concrete pressure times the waler spacing in feet (800 x 25/12 = 1667 pounds per foot). Using 2-inch x 4-inch double walers over four or more supports, the walers must be supported at 24-inch intervals, figure 15-4, page 113.

   Note: The amount of 1667 pounds per foot falls between 1600 pounds per foot with ties spaced at 25-inch spans and 1800 pounds per foot with ties spaced at 23-inch spans. Therefore, ties should be spaced at 24-inch intervals for 1667 pounds per foot.

4. To determine tie design, the load on each tie must be calculated. The load on each tie equals the load on the double walers times the tie spacing in feet (1667 x 24/12 = 3334 pounds). The ties must have an allowable load of at least 3334 pounds. If they do not, they must be spaced accordingly.

   Note: Most ties exceed the allowable load of 3334 pounds.

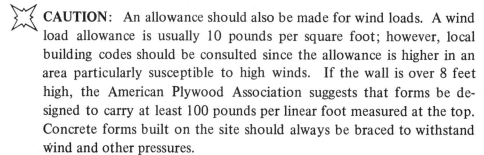 **CAUTION**: An allowance should also be made for wind loads. A wind load allowance is usually 10 pounds per square foot; however, local building codes should be consulted since the allowance is higher in an area particularly susceptible to high winds. If the wall is over 8 feet high, the American Plywood Association suggests that forms be designed to carry at least 100 pounds per linear foot measured at the top. Concrete forms built on the site should always be braced to withstand wind and other pressures.

FORM MATERIALS

Concrete forms built on the site are constructed of wood. The framing, walers, and braces are usually constructed of 2-inch x 4-inch stock which can be utilized later for studs in the framing of the structure. However, 2-inch x 6-inch stock is sometimes used when heavier forms are needed. At one time, tongue and groove or shiplap lumber was used for the sheathing; however, they are rarely used now because of the weight and the time involved in constructing a form with this material. Instead, plywood is used for the sheathing. Plywood can be utilized in later construction for rough flooring or wall sheathing.

CAUTION: All materials used in concrete form construction must be of good quality, straight, and smooth.

Estimating Materials

The following is a simple method used to estimate the form materials needed for the construction of a foundation wall.

1. Determine the perimeter of the building and multiply by 2 to obtain the measurements for both inside and outside forms. To determine the perimeter, add the outside dimensions for the total distance around the building. For example, the distance around a 32-foot x 48-foot structure is 160 feet. Two times 160 feet is 320 feet, the total distance around both the outside and the inside of the foundation.

2. Determine the height of the foundation. Assume that the foundation wall in this example is 8 feet high.

3. Determine the number of plywood sheets needed to sheath the frames. Plywood is available in various sizes of sheets. The most common size is 4 feet x 8 feet. For the 8-foot foundation wall, divide the total number of feet needed for the distance around the inside and outside foundation by 4 feet to obtain the required number of plywood sheets (320 ÷ 4 = 80). Therefore, 80 plywood sheets, measuring 4 feet x 8 feet each, are needed.

   Note: If the foundation is 4 feet or less, do not cut the sheets if the plywood is to be used in later construction. Instead, turn the plywood on edge so that the face veneer lays across the supporting studs. If the plywood is above the top of the foundation, the top of the foundation can be marked by nailing a strip along the plywood at the indicated position or by snapping a chalk line along the top. In this case, divide the total number of feet around the inside and outside of the foundation by 8 feet to estimate the required material.

   Note: Although the inside concrete form is smaller than the outside form because of the wall thickness, the same number of plywood sheets must be ordered for both the inside and the outside wall forms because the inside corner sheets must be cut to fit.

The number of 2-inch x 4-inch boards used for the framing and bracing can also be estimated.

1. To estimate the number of 2-inch x 4-inch studs 8 feet long used in framing, multiply the number of plywood sheets by the number of framing members on each panel. For the above example, each 4-foot x 8-foot plywood sheet is framed by five and one-half 8-foot boards, figure 15-5, page 116. If eighty plywood sheets are needed, 440 8-foot boards are needed for framing. When framing foundation walls less than 8 feet high, do not cut the studs. They can then be used later. The studs can be allowed to extend above the top of the sheathing.

2. Longer stock is used for the walers. Lumber 16 feet long is preferred, since the pieces can be cut in half and used for studs. For example, if the rafter length is 16 feet, 2-inch x 4-inch boards 16 feet long are used for the walers. To determine the number of boards for walers, divide the measurement taken around the foundation wall in feet (both inside and outside) by the waler length. This gives the number of boards needed to encompass the forms once. Multiply this number by the number of rows of walers. For example, if the distance around the inside and outside foundation wall is 320 feet, divide that figure by 16 feet for a total of twenty 2-inch x 4-inch boards each 16 feet long to circle the foundation once. Assuming that there are four rows of double walers, multiply by 8 for a total of 160 2-inch x 4-inch boards each 16 feet long to be used for walers.

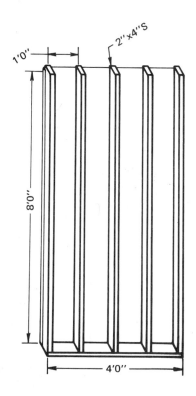

Fig. 15-5 Panel construction details.

3. Wooden forms should be braced as in figure 15-6. Generally, a brace every 4 feet for an 8-foot wall is sufficient for residential construction. Each brace for an 8-foot wall is constructed of a 2-inch x 4-inch board 10 feet long and a 2-inch x 4-inch board 8 feet long. If the form is braced every 4 feet, divide the distance around the forms by 4. For the example, divide 320 by 4 for a total of 80 braces. Therefore, eighty 2-inch x 4-inch boards 10 feet long and eighty 2-inch x 4-inch boards 8 feet long are needed. If a fairly low foundation form without walers is being constructed, the form should be braced at each framing stud, figure 15-7, page 117.

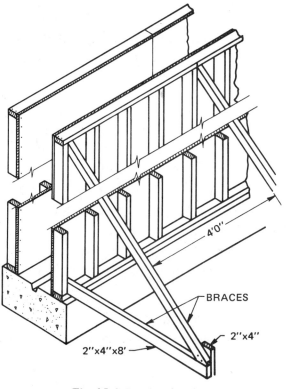

Fig. 15-6 Bracing details.

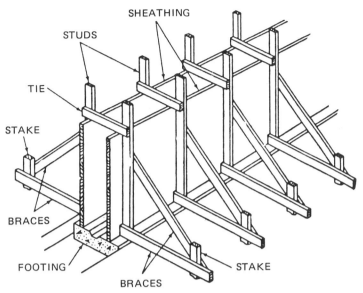

STUDS

SHEATHING

TIE

STAKE

BRACES

FOOTING

STAKE

BRACES

Fig. 15-7 Bracing low foundation walls.

4. To estimate the total number of boards, add the number of boards needed for framing, walers, and braces. In the example, 520 8-foot boards eighty 10-foot boards, and 160 16-foot boards are needed.

CONSTRUCTING THE WALL FORM

1. Nail the 2-inch edge of the sole plate along the back side of the plywood sheet with 6d nails, as shown in figure 15-5, page 116. For 8-foot walls, use plywood sheets 4 feet x 8 feet. For low foundation walls, turn the plywood on edge so that the face grain is across the supports. If the wall is less than 4 feet, mark the top of the foundation wall by nailing a narrow strip along the plywood sheet at the correct height or by snapping a chalk line at the right height. If the plywood is to be used in later construction, it is better to mark the sheet rather than to cut it. Concrete is then placed to the mark and leveled.

2. Nail supporting studs on each side of the plywood to both the plywood and the sole plate.

   CAUTION: It is very important that all sides are straight and corners square so that the panels fit tightly.

3. Measure and mark the spacing for supporting studs. Spacing is taken on center. Nail the supporting studs to the back of the plywood. This completes the panel. Continue this process until all panels except the corner filler panels are completed.

   Note: Do not construct the filler panels until all other panels are in position. Exact measurements can be better determined.

4. Notch the panels for ties at the proper spacing. Ties with rubber cups or wood cones which fit against the sheathing are designed specifically for forms built on site. These ties are usually ordered for a specific wall thickness. Notch the panels by drilling holes in the panel at the designated intervals. If a foundation wall 3 feet or less in height is being erected, no ties are needed. A spreader across the top and a brace at the bottom is a sufficient method.

CAUTION: Do not cut the notches too large or concrete leakage may result.

5. Lay the panels on the ground on each side of the footing.

6. The building lines indicating the position of the outside wall should already be in place. Snap a chalk line along the footing to mark the outside foundation position.

7. Erect the outside form panels by nailing the forms together with duplex-head nails.

8. Brace the forms as shown in figures 15-6, page 116 and 15-7, page 117.

9. Position and secure the walers and ties on the outside forms. Since there are numerous ties manufactured, the assembly directions for the tie being used should be followed.

CAUTION: Select good quality, straight stock for walers so that the form walls are properly aligned.

10. Erect the inside wall forms. Position the ties as each panel is erected.

    Note: Ties may be purchased for a specific wall thickness. When building concrete forms on the site, this type of tie is a tremendous aid when placing the inside wall forms.

11. Measure and build the corner filler panels. Nail into position.

    Note: Clean out any dirt or debris inside the form with a long-handled brush or broom before the filler panel is fastened into place. It is sometimes practical to wash the form out with a hose.

12. Check the forms before the concrete is poured.

    A. Check the levelness of the top of the concrete form with a builder's level, builder's transit, or carpenter's spirit level.

    B. Check the plumbness of the walls with a builder's transit or a carpenter's spirit level placed vertically against the side of the wall at frequent intervals.

       Note: A builder's level cannot be used to check if the wall is plumb because it does not have a vertical movement.

    C. Check the corners with a builder's level or builder's transit to ensure that they are square. Corners can also be checked by the 6-8-10 method. To use this method, measure 6 feet from the corner along one side and mark. Measure 8 feet from the corner along the other side and mark. Measure the third leg of the triangle from mark to mark. If the corner forms a 90-degree angle, the third leg of the triangle will measure 10 feet.

13. Pour the concrete. Concrete is delivered in ready-mix trucks and poured directly into the forms through a chute. As the concrete is poured, it is vibrated by turning a shovel in a vertical motion or tapping the sides with a hammer. This action evenly distributes the aggregates and eliminates air pockets.

    Note: Forming for window and door openings are installed before the concrete is poured. The procedure for these and anchoring methods will be discussed later.

14. The top surface is troweled till the desired finish is obtained. The top must be level.

    Note: Be sure to cure the concrete adequately. Curing time varies with weather conditions.

15. Remove the concrete forms and break back the tie projections. Fill and smooth any indentions or rough areas with cement grout or mortar for a smooth surface finish.

16. Form a cement cove at the base of the wall where it joins the footing so that water cannot collect in the corner, figure 15-8. Dampproof the foundation wall by applying two coats of hot bituminous mixture on the wall to the grade line. If the foundation is in a wet area, apply two 1/4-inch coats of cement plaster to the wall before the hot bituminous mixture is applied.

17. Install the perimeter drain tile.

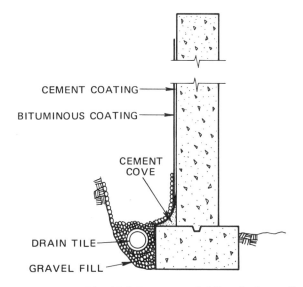

CEMENT COATING
BITUMINOUS COATING
CEMENT COVE
DRAIN TILE
GRAVEL FILL

Fig. 15-8 Dampproofed foundation wall.

APPLICATION

Complete each statement with the correct word or words.

1. The maximum support spacing for 3/4-inch Class I Plyform with the face grain parallel to the supports and with a maximum concrete pressure of 660 psf is _____ inch (inches).

2. _____ are used to align concrete forms and provide support to the structure.

3. If the load on the walers is 2200 pounds per foot and the ties are spaced 32 inches O.C., the ties must have an allowable load of _____ pound (pounds).

4. _____ is used for sheathing concrete forms built on the site.

5. The first step in estimating the number of plywood sheets needed for a concrete form is to determine the _____ of the structure.

6. The number of plywood sheets, each measuring 4 feet by 8 feet, needed for an 8-foot foundation wall on a 30-foot x 40-foot structure is _____.

7. When using concrete form materials in later construction the boards used for walers are usually _____ feet long.

8. Corner filler panels should not be constructed until all the other form panels are in position so that the _____ can be more accurately determined.

9. Check to be sure walls are _____ by placing a carpenter's spirit level vertically against the wall at frequent intervals.

10. As concrete is placed, it should be vibrated to distribute the _____ and eliminate _____.

Unit 16   Erecting Prefabricated Forms

OBJECTIVES

After studying this unit, the student will be able to

- differentiate between monolithic and standard foundation forms.
- list the procedures to follow when erecting foundation wall forms.
- estimate concrete for a foundation.

Residential contractors who build numerous foundations usually use prefabricated concrete forms in the interest of economy, and as a time-saving factor. There are numerous forming systems manufactured which can be either bought or rented.

With increasing specialization in the building trades, it is becoming common practice in many areas for a foundation contractor to erect the foundation and a building contractor to do the carpentry work. Foundation contractors work with a specialized crew who erect concrete forms, place reinforcement rods, pour concrete, set the anchoring devices in position, remove the forms, and finish the concrete surface. After these procedures are completed, the foundation is ready for the building of the structure.

Foundation contractors use prefabricated forms almost exclusively because they are more efficient, thereby saving a substantial amount of time and labor. Prefabricated forms can also be used repeatedly for an indefinite number of pourings if proper maintenance procedures are observed.

There are numerous forming systems on the market. Prefabricated concrete form panels are generally constructed of metal or metal frames with plywood faces. Forming systems come equipped with special hardware and accessories.

It would not be possible, within the scope of this text, to cover every forming system on the market today. General information and instructions representative of various types of forming systems will be discussed.

MONOLITHIC FORMS

The monolithic form, figure 16-1, page 122, is designed so that the footing and wall can be poured at one time. Monolithic forms are used primarily in the building of low foundations. They are practical for the contractor who builds numerous foundations with crawl spaces. Because the footing and wall are poured in one operation, the contractor is not required to wait for the footing to cure before the foundation wall is erected. One operation means a great amount of time and labor saved not only in the pouring, but in the erecting and stripping of the form.

Monolithic forms are secured at the top and bottom by flat ties which slip over panel pins, figure 16-2, page 122. The ties are designed so that forms for specific sizes of walls and footings may be fastened. The ties are also designed so that they may be removed and reused along with the forms. The forms and ties can be used for an indefinite number of

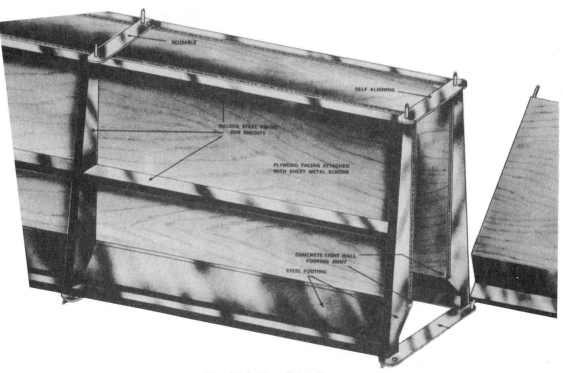

Fig. 16-1 Monolithic form.
Courtesy of Proctor Products Company, Incorporated

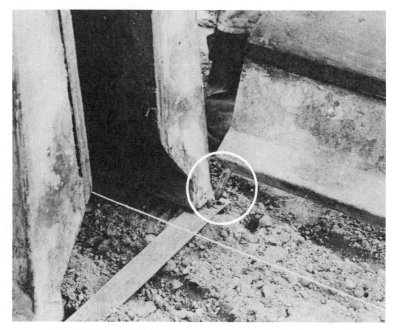

Fig. 16-2 Panel pins being inserted through the bottom tie.
Courtesy of Proctor Products Company, Incorporated

Fig. 16-3 First corner erected.

Courtesy of Proctor Products Company, Incorporated

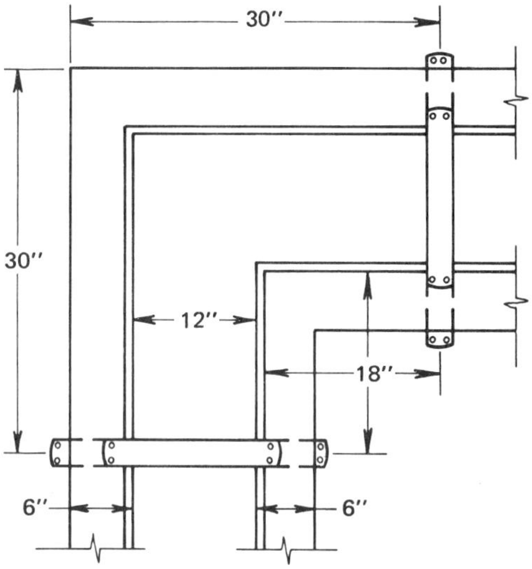

Fig. 16-4 Corner detail.

pourings. If the forms are constructed with metal frames and plywood sheathing, the plywood can be removed and replaced when it becomes damaged or worn.

ERECTING MONOLITHIC FORMS

1. Establish the location of the building lines. If batter boards are used, locate the outside corners with a plumb bob attached to the intersection of the building lines. If batter boards are not used, locate the building lines.

2. Stake the outside corners of the foundation. Place a nail in the top of the stake at the exact position of the outside corner of the foundation. Stretch a taut line between the stakes so that the building lines are close to the working area.

3. Set the first corner in place, figure 16-3. The corner consists of both the outside and inside corner panel and two standard ties, figure 16-4.

4. Set the rest of the panels in position along the building lines. Inside and outside panels are positioned at the same time because they are locked together with a top and a bottom tie. Place the bottom tie in position on the ground and insert the panel pins through the tie. Lock it into position with the top tie, figure 16-5, page 124.

   Note: Panels are self-aligning since they are fastened together with one tie at the top and one tie at the bottom, fastening four panels. However, it is important that the panels be set in a straight line along the building line.

5. If the form is higher than the top of the foundation, measure and mark the position of the top of the foundation at each inside corner. Snap

Fig. 16-5 Fastening the tops of the panels with the tie, which is inserted over the panel pins.
Courtesy of Proctor Products Company, Incorporated

Fig. 16-6 Troweling the wet concrete to obtain the desired surface finish. It is very important that the top be level; otherwise, adjustments will be required throughout construction.
Courtesy of Proctor Products Company, Incorporated

a chalk line along each inside wall of the form to establish the top of the foundation for pouring.

6. Install reinforcement rods, placing the short rods vertically in the soil. Tie two Number 5 reinforcement rods horizontally to the short rods. Three inches of concrete should surround the horizontal rods.

    Note: Vent bucks are installed at this point. (Vent bucks and anchoring devices will be covered in later units.)

7. Pour the concrete. Concrete is delivered in a ready-mix truck and poured directly into the forms. Pouring concrete into a monolithic form is simple because there are no ties to impede the flow of the concrete. Concrete should be vibrated or consolidated by working a shovel through the concrete in a vertical motion. This ensures uniform distribution of aggregates and eliminates any air pockets created in pouring.

    Note: Work the shovel between the form and the concrete to eliminate honeycombing on the face of the wall. (*Honeycombing* refers to concrete which has been poorly mixed and contains open spaces.)

8. Trowel or float the wet concrete until the top is level and the desired surface finish is obtained, figure 16-6.

9. After the concrete has cured, remove nails where vent bucks are held in place. Remove the top tie, figure 16-7, page 125. Pull the form panels straight back from the wall and out of the bottom ties. The bottom ties can be pulled from under the footing with a tie puller.

10. Clean the forms thoroughly with water and a stiff-bristled brush. Repair any damaged areas on the forms immediately. Oil or coat the forms with a release agent to prepare them for reuse.

Fig. 16-7 Removing the top ties with a small bar.
Courtesy of Proctor Products Company, Incorporated

Fig. 16-8 Panels placed around the footing, ready to be erected.

STANDARD FORMS

Foundations poured in standard prefabricated forms are poured in a two-phase operation. In the first phase, the footing forms are erected, leveled, and the footing is poured. Caution should be exercised to ensure that the footing is accurately leveled and that the surface is screeded or troweled to a smooth finish. This precaution will ensure a relatively trouble-free procedure when erecting the wall forms. After the footing is poured and the concrete cured, the concrete forms for the foundation walls are erected.

ERECTING STANDARD FORMS

1. Establish the building lines. Snap a chalk line along the footing to indicate the position of the outside foundation wall. Lay the panels around the footing so that they are ready to be set into place, figure 16-8. Panels are constructed with a 1 1/2-inch to 2-inch frame so that they may be set upright and remain in position with little effort.

   CAUTION: Panel faces should be free of defects and coated with a release agent.

2. Establish a corner location and erect the outside corner section, figure 16-9, page 126. Note the design of the corner panels and the two filler panels which are the width of the wall thickness plus the width of the inside corner form.

3. Fasten the outside corner form in place, using the fastening hardware which accompanies the forming system. The forming system shown in figure 16-9, page 126, is fastened by wedge bolts using the following steps.

    A.   Insert panel ties through the tie slots.

    B.   Insert a wedge bolt through the adjoining panel and the tie loop or slot.

    C.   Insert a second wedge bolt through the first bolt. The assembly is tightened by lightly tapping the head of the horizontal wedge bolt with a hammer.

    Note: Insert wedge bolts from left to right so that they may be removed with a blow with a hammer in the right hand.

4. Continue setting up and fastening the outside panels until all outside panels, ties, and hardware are in position.

5. Position the walers to align and support the forms. Braces should also be positioned as needed at this point.

    A.   Place the waler tie in the tie slot.

    ☆ **CAUTION**: Do not put the waler tie under the head of a connecting bolt at a tie location.

    B.   Place walers over and under the waler tie. Slip the tie holder over the waler tie loop. Lock the walers into position with the wedge bolt, figure 16-10, page 127. Waler clamps are available which can be used to hold the walers in position.

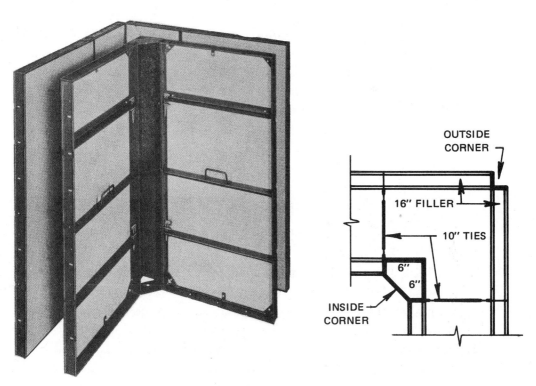

Fig. 16-9 Corner detail.
Courtesy of Symons Corporation

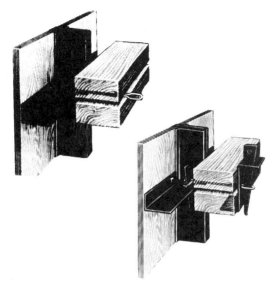

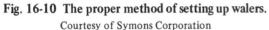

Fig. 16-11 Outside form in place, with ties and reinforcement rods ready for the next inside form to be erected.

Fig. 16-10 The proper method of setting up walers.

Courtesy of Symons Corporation

Courtesy of Mid-Missouri Company

C. Brace the forms as required. Braces and brace plates which simplify this procedure are available. Tall forms or forms erected in an area susceptible to high winds should be braced; however, low forms generally do not need bracing.

Note: Walers and braces should be used as needed to align and support the outside forms.

6. Erect the inside forms following the above procedure. The inside wall forms are automatically positioned with ties designed for a specific wall thickness. Inside panels should be the same width as the opposing outside panel.

Note: Number 5 or 5/8-inch reinforcement rods should be placed horizontally as the panels are positioned. The number of reinforcement rods depends on the stability of the soil. Generally, two horizontal rods at the top and two horizontal rods near the bottom are sufficient. Figure 16-11 shows the outside form in place with the ties and reinforcement rods ready for the next inside panel which is to be erected.

7. Check the forms to be sure that they are level, fit tightly, and are aligned.

Note: If any dirt or debris is inside the form, remove it before the concrete is poured.

8. Pour the concrete. Vibrate or consolidate the concrete as previously discussed. Vibrating machines are available to mechanically vibrate the concrete as it is being poured; however, most residential concrete work can be consolidated with a shovel or a 2-inch x 4-inch piece of lumber.

9. Remove the forms. Break the ties and finish the wall surface with mortar or cement plaster.

10. Waterproof the foundation wall. Form a cove of cement plaster around the outside perimeter of the foundation wall where the footing and foundation wall meet. This prevents water from collecting in the angle. Apply two coats of hot bituminous mixture on the foundation wall to the grade line.

    Note: If the foundation soil is in a wet area, two 1/4-inch coats of cement plaster should be applied to the foundation wall before the hot bituminous mixture is applied.

11. Install the drain tile as discussed in Unit 4.

12. Clean the forms thoroughly with water and a stiff wire brush. If there are any damaged areas, repair them immediately. Treat the form panels with oil or a release agent to prepare them for the next pour.

Prefabricated concrete forms are extremely adaptable. They are easily erected for curved wall forms. Some forming systems are available with small metal filler panels which can be used to form a curve. Other forming systems use filler angles with plywood strips. Modern concrete forming materials simplify the procedure so that few forming jobs present serious problems.

 CAUTION: Forming systems are available with hardware and accessories designed for each specific system; therefore, the directions for each individual forming system must be followed.

ESTIMATING CONCRETE

Concrete is delivered to the site in ready-mix trucks from a concrete company; however, the contractor must be able to determine the concrete needed before an order can be placed. Concrete is sold in cubic yards. To estimate the cubic yards of concrete needed for a specific foundation, use the formula

perimeter (in feet) times wall height (in feet) times wall width (in feet) equals cubic feet divided by 27. (There are 27 cubic feet in 1 cubic yard.)

For example, determine the cubic yards of concrete needed for a house which measures 24 feet by 40 feet with a foundation wall 8 feet high and 8 inches thick:

- $(2 \times 24) + (2 \times 40) = 128$-foot perimeter
- $128 \times 8 \times 8/12 = 682.67$ cubic feet $\div 27 = 25.28$ cubic yards of concrete
- Add 5 to 10 percent for waste. In the example, 10 percent of the total is 2.53 cubic yards; 2.53 plus 25.28 equals 27.8 cubic yards of concrete needed for the foundation wall. When ordering, this would be rounded off to 28 cubic yards.

APPLICATION

Complete each statement with the correct word or words.

1. A concrete form designed so that the footing and foundation wall can be poured at one time is known as a _____ form.

2. Monolithic forms are used primarily for _____ foundations.

3. If the form is higher than the top of the foundation wall, it should be marked along the inside form at the designated height with a _____.

4. Wet concrete should be vibrated or consolidated as it is poured to distribute the _____ and eliminate _____ caused by the pouring.

5. All forms should be treated with a _____ to prevent the panels from adhering to the concrete.

6. For foundations poured in standard concrete forms, the _____ is poured in the first phase and the _____ is poured in the second phase.

7. Inside form panels should be the same width as the _____ outside panel.

8. Since modern forming systems may differ to a great extent, _____ for each individual forming system must be followed.

9. The amount (in cubic yards) of concrete needed for a structure which measures 30 feet by 40 feet with a foundation 8 feet high and 10 inches thick is _____. Allow 10 percent of the total for waste.

10. _____ are slipped over panel pins to secure monolithic forms at the top and bottom.

Unit 17   Anchoring Methods

OBJECTIVES

After studying this unit, the student will be able to

- identify anchoring hardware.
- list procedures followed when anchoring a structure to the foundation.

Structures must be anchored to concrete foundations to prevent the structures from shifting. Provisions for anchoring wooden framework to concrete foundations are usually made at the time the foundation is poured. Local building codes should always be consulted before anchoring devices are installed. Wind is a predominant cause of shifting; therefore, building codes in areas susceptible to hurricanes, tornadoes, or unusually high winds frequently specify stronger anchoring methods than other areas.

ANCHORING HARDWARE

Anchoring hardware is used to anchor the structure to the foundation. One anchoring device which is frequently used is a simple threaded anchor bolt with a washer and nut on one end. The bolt is designed with a head or curve on one end which anchors it in the concrete, figure 17-1. The head or curve lend strength to the bolt, preventing it from becoming dislodged under pressure. The bolts, available with a 1/2-inch or 3/4-inch diameter are placed in the concrete at evenly spaced intervals 4 to 8 feet apart. The washer and nut are placed over the sill, tightening it in place, figure 17-2, page 131.

Another commonly used anchoring device is a heavy, zinc-coated, steel anchoring clip, figure 17-3, page 131. This is a very simple, efficient anchoring device for residential structures. The anchor clip is designed with arms which can be shaped as desired, figure 17-4, page 131. The anchor clips are shipped flat and shaped when they are installed. The lower arms are spread apart to provide an anchor in the concrete. The upper arms are formed to fit around the mud sill and are nailed to it.

Certain anchor bolts may be installed after the concrete has cured. In this method,

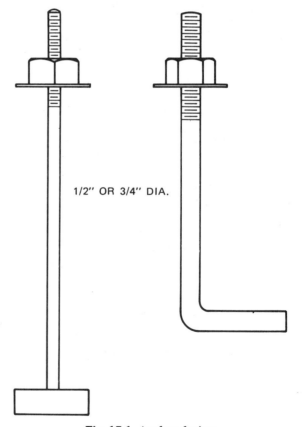

1/2" OR 3/4" DIA.

Fig. 17-1 Anchor devices.

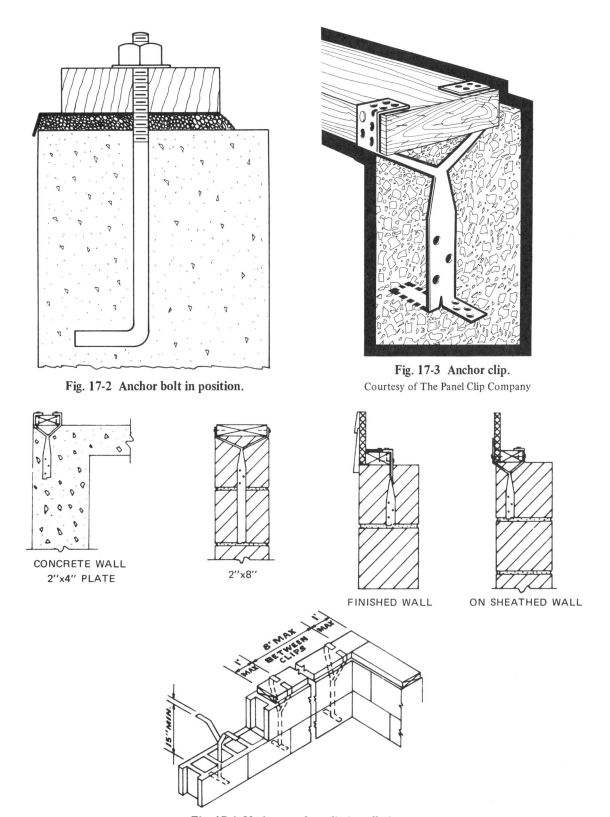

Fig. 17-2 Anchor bolt in position.

Fig. 17-3 Anchor clip.
Courtesy of The Panel Clip Company

CONCRETE WALL
2"x4" PLATE

2"x8"

FINISHED WALL

ON SHEATHED WALL

8' MAX
BETWEEN
CLIPS

1"
MAX

1"
MAX

15" MIN.

Fig. 17-4 Various anchor clip installations.
Courtesy of The Panel Clip Company

a hole the size of the diameter of the anchor bolt is drilled. The bolt is driven into the hole with a hammer until at least 6 threads are below the top surface of the concrete. The washer and nut are then placed on the bolt and the unit is tightened with the nut. Installation procedures for Hilti Kwik-Bolts®, an anchoring device of this type, is illustrated in figure 17-5(A). These anchoring devices are available with a round head, a hexagonal head, or a countersink flat head, figure 17-5(B). Various sizes of Kwik-Bolts® with their average pullout and shear strength measurements are shown in figure 17-6(A) and (B), page 133.

ANCHORING SUPPORTING COLUMNS

Supporting columns must also be anchored to prevent them from slipping off the footing. Wooden columns may be anchored with a steel pin or reinforcement rod placed vertically in the wet concrete. The column is then positioned by drilling a hole in the column and positioning it over the pin, figure 17-7, page 133. Wooden supporting columns can also be anchored with post anchors such as the post base clip, figure 17-8, page 133. The post is positioned in the anchor and the sides are nailed to the post. Note the holes in the bottom which allow the base to be nailed to the concrete with concrete nails, or an anchoring device to be driven into the concrete. The plate is also designed with weep holes to eliminate moisture accumulation. The cap in figure 17-8, page 133, is placed in the base to hold the column off the base and away from the moisture, figure 17-9, page 134.

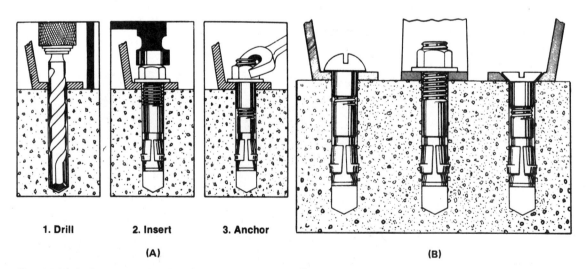

| 1. Drill | 2. Insert | 3. Anchor |

(A)   (B)

Fig. 17-5(A) shows installation of the Hilti Kwik-Bolt®, an anchor bolt which may be installed after concrete has cured. (B) shows various types of heads available.

Courtesy of McCulloch Industries, Copyrighted by Hilti Fastening Systems, Incorporated

Fig. 17-6(A) Various sizes of Kwik-Bolts. The steel spring wedge on the masonry end of the bolt grips the concrete to provide better holding power.

Courtesy of McCulloch Industries, copyrighted by Hilti Fastening Systems, Incorporated

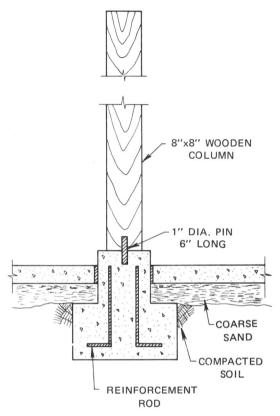

Fig. 17-7 Wooden column anchored to stepped footing.

AVERAGE PULLOUT & SHEAR STRENGTH MEASUREMENTS

Diameter	3500 PSI CONCRETE		5500 PSI CONCRETE	
	Pullout (Lbs.)	Shear (Lbs.)	Pullout (Lbs.)	Shear (Lbs.)
¼ "	3,093	2,050	3,560	2,300
⅜ "	4,267	5,400	5,667	6,200
½ "	8,267	8,840	9,633	9,000
⅝ "	16,667	13,800	19,533	15,100
¾ "	23,633	19,900	28,400	20,000

Maximum loads should not exceed ¼ of the above values.

Fig. 17-6(B) Average pullout and shear strength measurements.

Fig. 17-8 Post base clip.
Courtesy of The Panel Clip Company

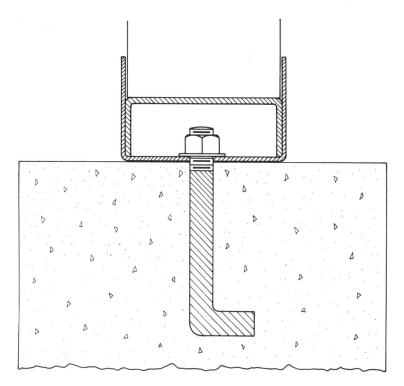

Fig. 17-9 Post clip in position.

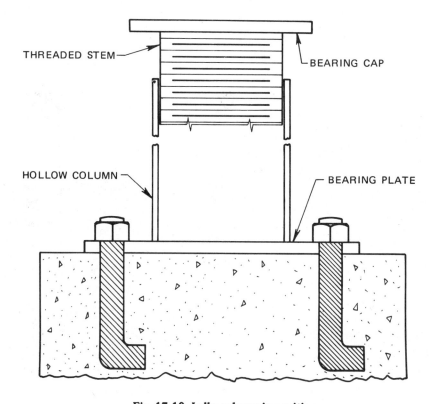

THREADED STEM

BEARING CAP

HOLLOW COLUMN

BEARING PLATE

Fig. 17-10 Lally column in position.

Lally columns are manufactured with a steel bearing plate to anchor the column to the footing. The bearing plate has holes so that it can be anchored with a standard anchor bolt, figure 17-10, page 134.

Concrete piers are anchored to the footing by reinforcement rods which are placed vertically in the footing when it is poured. After the footing has cured sufficiently, the column or pier is poured over and around the reinforcement rods.

INSTALLING ANCHORING DEVICES

1. Determine the location of the anchor bolt or anchor clip from blueprint specifications. Anchor bolts which measure 1/2 inch to 3/4 inch are usually placed in the center of the sill at 4- to 8-foot intervals, beginning one foot from the end with a minimum of two bolts per sill.

CAUTION: Anchoring devices should be placed so that they do not interfere with the floor joists.

2. As soon as the concrete has been troweled and leveled, measure and mark the position of the first anchoring device.

3. Place the anchoring device in the wet concrete with the bolt extending above the top of the foundation. Leave enough space for the grout, termite shield, sill, and washer and nut. Work the bolt around in the wet concrete just enough to eliminate air pockets and to seat the bolt. Trowel around the bolt to smooth the surface. The concrete is stiff enough to hold the anchoring device in position, figure 17-11.

Note: If anchor clips are being used, bend the lower arms until they are perpendicular to the body of the clip before it is placed in the concrete.

Fig. 17-11 Anchor bolts positioned in wet concrete.
Courtesy of Mid-Missouri Company

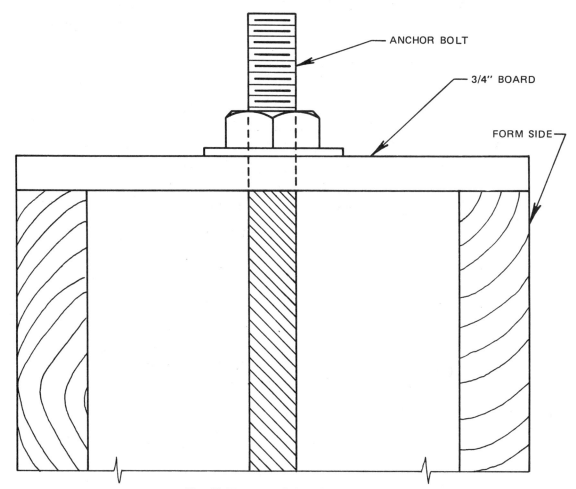

Fig. 17-12 Suspended anchor bolt.

4. Continue measuring and placing each anchoring device until the foundation is complete. The same procedure is followed when installing anchor bolts for supporting columns.

   Note: If the anchor bolts are the type which are installed by drilling, they are installed after the concrete has cured.

   Note: Some builders suspend the anchoring device in the form and then pour the concrete around the bolt or clip. The bolt is held in position by a piece of stock nailed to the concrete form at the correct position, figure 17-12. If this procedure is followed, check the bolts to be sure that they are not pushed out of place by the wet concrete.

APPLICATION

Complete each statement with the correct word or words.

1. Buildings must be anchored to the concrete foundation to prevent them from _____.

2. A (An) _____ with a curve or head on one end and a washer and a nut on the other end is frequently used to anchor the framing of a structure to the foundation.

3. The head or the curve on the end of the bolt prevents the bolt from being _____ under pressure.

4. An anchoring device which can be shaped to fit around the sill and anchor in concrete is a (an) _____ .

5. When using the type of anchor bolt which is installed after the concrete has cured, a hole must be _____ into the concrete.

6. Wooden columns may be anchored with a (an) _____ or _____ placed vertically in the footing.

7. Concrete piers are anchored to the footing with _____ .

8. An anchoring device may be installed by placing the device in the _____ and working the bolt to eliminate the air pockets and seat the bolt.

9. Anchoring devices may be _____ in concrete forms, with wet concrete poured around the bolt or clip.

10. _____ columns are manufactured with a steel bearing plate which anchors the column to the footing.

Section 5

Pier Construction

Unit 18   Pier Footings

OBJECTIVES

After studying this unit, the student will be able to

- figure dimensions of pier footings.
- differentiate between pier footing designs.
- construct pier footings.

Piers or *columns* are designed to support concentrated structural weight. Most residential structures with basements are constructed with wooden supporting beams or lally columns in the center of the basement. Residential structures with a crawl space may have supporting beams of concrete piers or concrete block. Each supporting beam or column must rest on a pier footing large enough to distribute the concentrated weight over a sufficient area.

In addition to the supporting piers or lally columns used in a standard foundation, the foundation soil or topography may necessitate the construction of a pier foundation. A pier foundation is constructed with the foundation footing resting on a series of piers which support the structural weight. Some pier foundations are constructed with a footing under the piers; others are constructed with cone-shaped piers which have sufficient width at the bottom to distribute the structural weight over the required area.

FOOTING DIMENSIONS

Each supporting pier or lally column is poured on a pier footing. To determine the correct size footing, the structural load that will eventually rest on a given pier or column must be figured. Pier specifications are usually given on the blueprints; however, the foundation contractor should be able to figure the footing size.

Footing dimensions are based on two factors, the structural load and the soil-bearing strength. The following is an example of the methods used to determine the structural load which rests on each pier. When following the steps, refer to figures 18-1 and 18-2, page 139.

1. Determine the area or the number of square feet that a given pier or column must support. The columns in figure 18-1 are placed at 7-foot intervals and support a 20-foot width. (Half the width of the structure is supported by exterior walls.) Therefore, column A must support an area 7 feet x 20 feet, or a total area of 140 square feet.

2. Determine the structural load per square foot which is exerted on a given pier or column.

   A. Live load for the attic is 20 pounds per square foot (light storage).

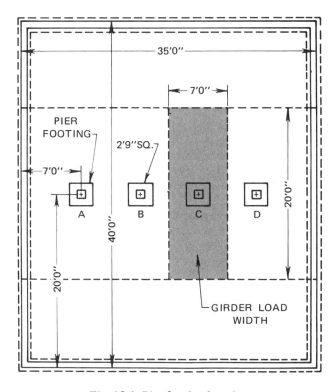

Fig. 18-1 Pier footing location.

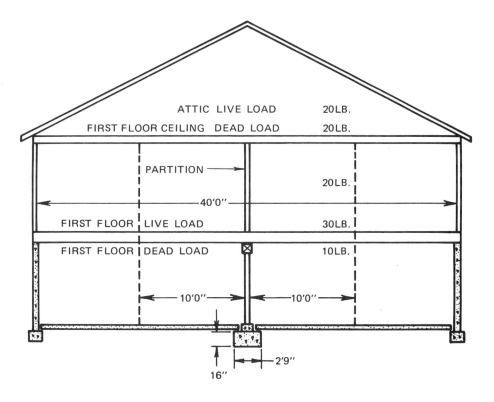

Fig. 18-2 Structural loads.

B.   Dead load of the first floor ceiling and plaster is 20 pounds per square foot.

C.   Dead load of partitions is 20 pounds per square foot.

D.   Live load of the first floor is 30 pounds per square foot.

E.   Dead load of the first floor is 10 pounds per square foot.

The combined structural weight is 100 pounds per square foot.

3.   Determine the total structural weight exerted on a given pier. The total structural weight exerted on column A in the example is determined by multiplying pounds per square foot by the area supported by column A: 100 pounds per square foot x 140 square feet = 14,000 pounds on column A.

4.   Determine the footing size by dividing the structural load that a given pier must support by the number of pounds the foundation soil is capable of supporting. Assume that the foundation soil is soft clay, which has a bearing strength of 2,000 pounds per square foot. To determine the footing size for column A, divide 14,000 pounds by 2,000 pounds which equals 7; therefore, 7 square feet of surface area is needed to support the structural load of column A. The pier footing in the example measures 33 inches x 33 inches x 16 inches. For most residential construction, a 2 foot to 3 foot square footing is sufficient for most supporting beams or piers. A standard thickness of one-half the footing width is adequate in most instances; therefore, a 12- to 18-inch thick footing is generally acceptable.

Note: Structural loads given in the example are generally accepted figures; however, local building codes should always be consulted to determine the specified structural load in a given area.

PIER FOOTING DESIGNS

Pier or column footings may be rectangular, stepped, tapered, or circular. The design is determined mostly by the size of the footing. The footing must be large enough to support the concentrated load exerted on the column or pier. Piers or columns are usually built to stand independently; however, they may be part of the foundation wall footing where a wall and column are combined to form a pilaster, or where a chimney or fireplace is installed on the outside wall. Pier footings should be reinforced because of the concentrated structural load on a relatively

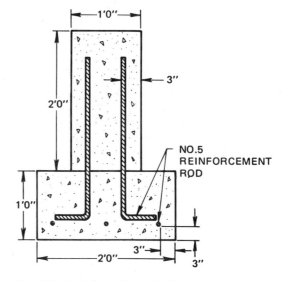

Fig. 18-3 Reinforced pier footing.

small area. There should be at least 3 inches of concrete on all sides of the reinforcement rods.

A simple rectangular footing, figure 18-3, page 140, can be used under a pier if the footing is large enough. Note the horizontal reinforcing rods. Vertical reinforcement rods are used to tie the footing and concrete piers together.

Rectangular footings are also used for chimneys or fireplaces. If the chimney or fireplace is on an outside wall, the footing is poured at the same time the foundation footing is poured. As with wall footings, fireplace and chimney footings must be placed below the frost line to prevent heaving. They must also be reinforced. Fireplace and chimney footings are usually reinforced by forming a horizontal grid with Number 5 reinforcement rods, figure 18-4. The footing size varies with the chimney or fireplace size and the soil-bearing properties; however, the footing for a chimney or fireplace in a two-story house should be at least 12 inches thick with a 6-inch minimum projection width.

Stepped footings, figure 18-5, page 142, can be used where the structural load per square foot is greater than the bearing strength of the soil. A *stepped footing* is simply a series of two or three decreasing single footings placed on top of each other to form steps. Reinforcement rods are used to strengthen these footings.

Stepped footings are also used under wooden supporting beams to raise the wooden beams above the basement floor level. This keeps the wood above the floor, thus eliminating moisture damage to the wooden beam.

Tapered footings can also be used to distribute the structural load over a wide area. Tapered sides are structurally sound and conserve concrete. The shear angle of concrete

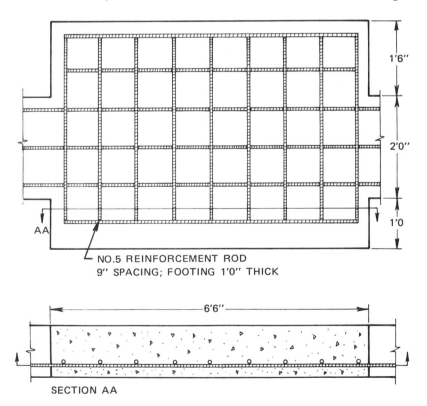

Fig. 18-4 Fireplace footing with reinforcement grid.

under stress is 45 degrees; therefore, the taper or slope of the sides must be greater than 45 degrees. The 60-degree angle on the tapered footing in figure 18-6 is generally considered an acceptable taper. This provides a 15-degree safety margin.

Circular footings can also be used under circular piers if they cover an area which sufficiently distributes the structural load. To determine the area covered by a circle, use the formula $A = \pi r^2$, where r is the radius and π is 3.14.

To determine the area of a circle with a radius of 1.5 feet, multiply 1.5 x 1.5 to obtain r^2, or 2.25 square feet. Multiply 2.25 by 3.14 which equals 7. Therefore, the area covered by a circle with a radius of 1.5 feet is 7 square feet. Prefabricated circular concrete pier forms are available, although circular concrete piers are rarely used in residential construction.

A pilaster is frequently constructed at points where a concentrated structural load will be exerted on the foundation wall. Pilaster footings are poured as an extension of the foundation wall footing, figure 18-7.

HOW TO CONSTRUCT A FOOTING FORM

Figure 18-8, page 143, shows a typical footing form.

1. Determine the location of the pier or column.

   A. Foundation piers are placed at intervals along the building line at specified depths.

   B. Footings for supporting beams are poured after foundation wall footings. The pier position can then be located by measuring from the wall footing and marking the center of the pier location with a stake.

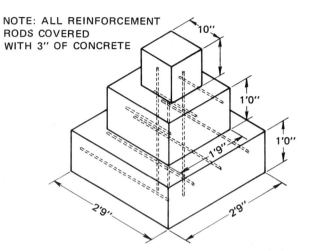

NOTE: ALL REINFORCEMENT RODS COVERED WITH 3" OF CONCRETE

Fig. 18-5 Stepped footing.

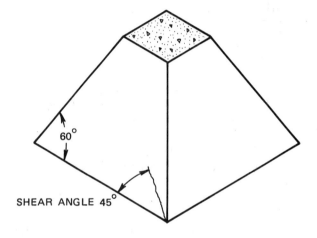

SHEAR ANGLE 45°

Fig. 18-6 Tapered footing.

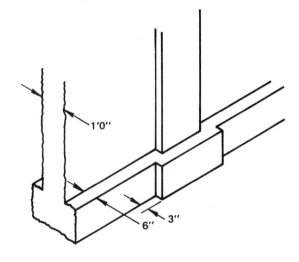

Fig. 18-7 Pilaster footing.

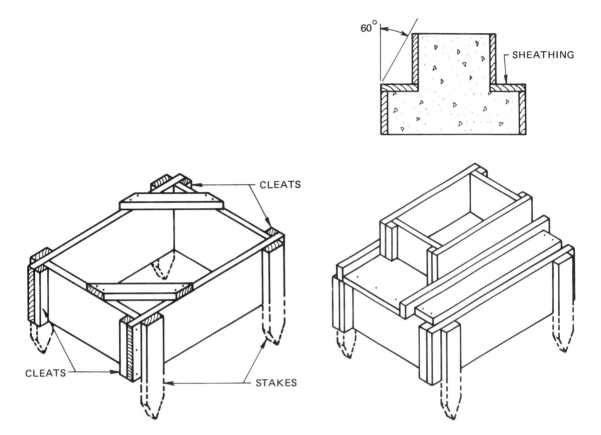

Fig. 18-8 Footing form construction.   Fig. 18-9 Stepped footing form construction.

✸ CAUTION: All footings, including pier footings under supporting beams, must be level and below the frost line.

2. Cut two pieces of stock in lengths corresponding to the width of the footing. Cut two pieces the length of the footing plus a 4-inch allowance for nailing to the corner cleats. Use 2-inch stock which is equal in width to the footing depth. The widest dimension of stock is 14 inches. If the footing is over 14 inches deep, the footing can be constructed of plywood cut to the necessary size or by using two boards to form a footing panel.

✸ CAUTION: If boards are nailed together, they must be tight so that wet concrete does not leak through the joints.

3. Cut cleats corresponding to the depth of the footing from stock which measures 2 inches x 4 inches. Cut four stakes from the same size stock.

4. Nail the four sides together to form the rectangular footing.

5. Place the form in position and drive a stake at each side to keep it from slipping when the concrete is poured.

6. Measure the footing form to be sure that the form is the correct size. Check the diagonals to be sure that the form is square. Place a brace across the top.

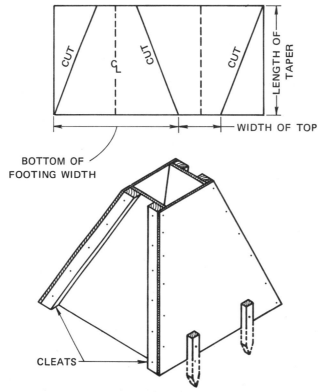

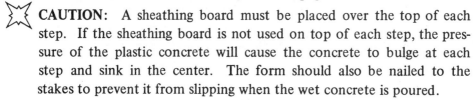

Fig. 18-10 Tapered footing construction.

Note: For a stepped footing, construct the necessary number of smaller footing forms following the procedures on page 143. Nail the smaller forms on top of the base form, figure 18-9, page 143.

CAUTION: A sheathing board must be placed over the top of each step. If the sheathing board is not used on top of each step, the pressure of the plastic concrete will cause the concrete to bulge at each step and sink in the center. The form should also be nailed to the stakes to prevent it from slipping when the wet concrete is poured.

7. Pour a 3-inch layer of concrete. Place the horizontal reinforcement rods in position. Finish pouring and positioning the vertical reinforcement rods or anchoring devices.

8. Trowel the wet concrete to a smooth, level surface.

9. After the concrete has cured, remove the forms carefully to avoid chipping the edges of the footing.

HOW TO CONSTRUCT THE TAPERED FOOTING FORM

Figure 18-10 shows a typical tapered footing form.

1. Determine the location of the pier or column.

2. Cut two sheets of plywood the length of the incline of the form. Measure the width at the bottom of the footing and make a mark. Working

from the center, measure the width at the top of the footing and make a mark.

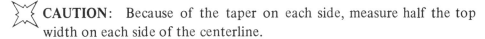 **CAUTION:** Because of the taper on each side, measure half the top width on each side of the centerline.

3. Mark off a straight taper between the top and the bottom panels and cut along these lines.

4. Cut cleats the length of the incline from 2-inch x 4-inch stock. Cut stakes from the same material.

5. Nail a cleat to each side of the plywood to form two panels.

6. Make two other panels following the above procedures, the only difference being to add a 2-inch allowance on each side of each piece for nailing the form together.

7. Nail the four sides together. Be certain that the joints are tight so that the concrete cannot leak.

8. Secure the form by nailing a brace across the top. To prevent the form from slipping and lifting when the wet concrete is placed, brace the sides by driving a stake into the ground on each side and nailing the stakes to the form.

9. Place the plastic concrete and install the reinforcing rods or anchoring devices.

10. Trowel the wet concrete to a smooth, level surface.

11. Remove the forms when the concrete has cured.

APPLICATION

Complete each statement with the correct word or words.

1. All supporting beams or lally columns should be constructed on a (an) _____.

2. Some pier foundations may be constructed with _____-shaped piers if they are sufficiently wide at the bottom to distribute structural weight.

3. Pier footing dimensions are based on two factors, the _____ and the _____.

4. The surface area needed to sufficiently distribute the weight of a column supporting 100 square feet of area, with a structural load of 160 pounds per square foot on soft clay is _____.

5. A 2-to-3 foot square pier footing with a (an) _____-inch depth is sufficient for most residential structures.

6. A combination wall and column form a (an) _____, with the footing poured with the foundation footing.

7. Fireplace and chimney footings for a two-story house must be at least _____ inches thick with a (an) _____-inch projection.

8. A series of single footings placed on top of each other to form steps is known as a (an) _____.

9. The shear angle of concrete is _____; therefore, the angle of a tapered footing is _____.

10. Stepped and tapered footing forms should be nailed to _____ to prevent them from slipping and lifting when the plastic concrete is placed.

Unit 19   Pier Forms

OBJECTIVES

After studying this unit, the student will be able to

- list situations in which concrete piers are most frequently used in residential construction.
- construct a concrete pier form.

After footings have cured, the piers or columns of a structure can be erected. Pier footings must be placed as a base for all supporting columns where a concentrated structural load is to rest on a given column or pier.

There are two main methods used to install supporting columns for basement structures. One method is to anchor wooden columns ranging in size from 6 inches x 8 inches to 8 inches x 10 inches to a pier footing. The second and most common method is to anchor steel lally columns to the pier footing for support.

Steel lally columns are hollow steel tubes with an adjustable threaded stem on top which enables the column to be adjusted as the structure settles. Lally columns may be used hollow or filled with concrete for added structural strength.

It is imperative that pier footings be placed below the frost line; therefore, if the frost line is below the basement floor level, a concrete pier or column must be poured to bridge the area between the footing and the supporting pier.

Independent concrete piers are frequently used for supporting columns under residential structures with a crawl space foundation; however, they are rarely used for basement foundations. Concrete piers are also used in residential construction when the foundation site necessitates the construction of a pier foundation. A pier foundation is constructed so that the foundation footing rests on a series of reinforced piers which support the structural weight, figure 19-1.

At times, pier foundations may be constructed on fill soil. Since fill soil shifts during the settling process, cavities under and around the foundation often result. The pressure of the shifting soil or the cavity may cause the foundation to shift and crack if the structural weight is forced to rest on the fill soil. One solution to this problem is to construct the foundation footing on a series of reinforced concrete piers or columns which are poured on original soil. The piers carry the weight to the

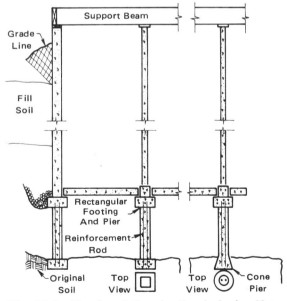

Fig. 19-1 **Pier foundation (sectional view).** *Note:* **Cone- or rectangular-shaped piers may be used.**

147

original soil, thereby providing a stable foundation base. Piers of this type are usually poured without a separate footing. Instead, a hole with a cone-shaped base is drilled to the required depth and a reinforced cone-shaped or tapered pier with a base wide enough to distribute the structural weight is poured. If the piers are drilled to a substantial depth for a foundation of this type, an architectural engineer should be consulted for pier specifications.

Pier foundations may also be used to solve problems encountered when the foundation footing depth falls within an unsuitable soil strata, such as very soft clay. Clay easily absorbs and holds water causing it to be very slippery, thereby possessing poor load-bearing strength. To avoid this problem, reinforced piers can be poured to a depth below the clay strata. The piers carry the structural weight to a more stable soil strata, lessening the stress on the foundation caused by the slippery clay.

Pier foundations can also be utilized on sloping sites to lend stability to the foundation. If the building site is steeply sloped and no retaining precautions are taken, there is a tendency for the structural load to shift to the lower level of the site. A series of reinforced piers evenly distributes the structural weight over the same level to eliminate this problem.

HOW TO CONSTRUCT A PIER

1. Determine pier specifications. These are usually contained in the blueprints, often known as *working drawings*. Since the compressive strength of concrete is high and usually exceeds the structural load, fairly short piers can be constructed in sizes corresponding to the foundation wall width. If relatively deep piers are needed for a pier foundation, an architectural engineer should be consulted to determine pier specifications.

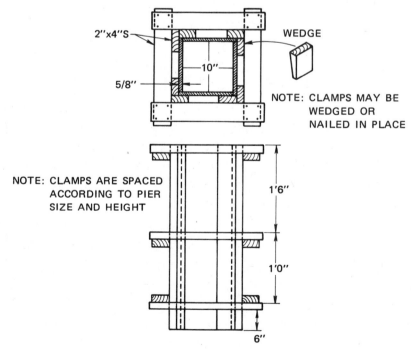

Fig. 19-2 Pier form construction.

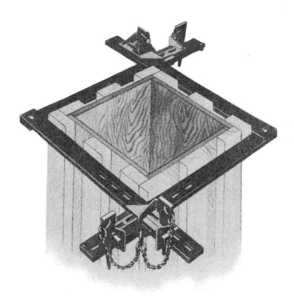

Fig. 19-3 Steel column clamp.
Courtesy of Symons Corporation

2. For each pier, cut four plywood sheets the width of the pier plus the thickness of the plywood to leave space for nailing the form together. Each sheet should be the height of the pier. For example, for a 10 inch x 10-inch x 4-foot pier using 5/8-inch plywood for the form facing, cut four sheets measuring 10 5/8 inches x 4 feet.

3. Cut bracing members from 2-inch x 4-inch stock. Each board length should correspond to the pier height.

4. Brace each plywood sheet with 2–inch x 4-inch boards. Allow one board on each panel to extend 1 1/2 inches over the side so that the panels can be nailed together, figure 19-2, page 148.

5. Nail the panels together. Check all measurements.

6. Build column clamps from 2–inch x 4-inch stock. Clamps should be placed at 12- to 20-inch intervals, with closer intervals at the bottom since this is where greater pressure is exerted. Adjustable steel column clamps, figure 19-3, are available for this purpose. Steel column clamps are strong and simple to position and remove. Because they are stronger than wood, they may be spaced at wider intervals.

Note: Deep piers under a pier foundation are often poured with a slightly tapered pier that is wide enough at the bottom to distribute the structural load. The forms for this type of pier are made following the above procedures, except for an allowance which is made for the taper.

Some builders drill a hole at the bottom in a cone shape. The hole is drilled to the depth of the pier and filled with concrete. This should be done only if the soil is a firm, compact soil; otherwise, concrete forms should be used to shore the sides.

Fig. 19-4 Circular pier form.
Courtesy of Proctor Products Company, Incorporated.

7. Place the reinforcement rods.

⟡ **CAUTION**: The compressive strength of concrete is high. However, its tensile strength is relatively low, approximately 11 percent of its compressive strength. Because of this, all concrete piers or beams should be reinforced with steel reinforcement rods.

8. Pour the wet concrete. Consolidate the concrete as it is poured by working a shovel up and down in the mixture to eliminate air pockets and distribute the aggregate.

9. Trowel the surface until it is smooth and level.

10. After the concrete has cured, carefully remove the forms to avoid chipping the concrete edges.

    Note: Concrete pier forms can be erected with prefabricated forms by the use of small panels, fillers, and corner sections. Metal circular forms of various sizes are available for low piers, figure 19-4. These are easily fastened and removed using the hardware that comes with the forming system. Other prefabricated column forms are available. However, they are usually heavy duty forms not used extensively in residential construction.

APPLICATION

Complete each statement with the correct word or words.

1. Concrete piers are frequently used for supporting columns in residential structures with a (an) _____ foundation.

2. When the frost line is below the basement floor level, a concrete pier must be poured to bridge the area between the _____ and the _____.

3. A pier foundation is constructed with the foundation footings resting on a series of _____.

4. Reinforced piers are used to carry structural weight to original soil when the structure is being erected on _____.

5. If no retaining precautions are taken on a sharply sloped site, there is a tendency for the structural load to shift to the _____.

6. A (An) _____ should be consulted if the foundation soil necessitates deep piers.

7. Because the tensile strength of concrete is relatively low, all concrete piers should be reinforced with _____.

8. Deep piers under a pier foundation are often poured with a pier which is slightly _____ and wide enough at the bottom to distribute the structural load.

9. Deep piers should be poured without forms only if the soil is a _____ type of soil.

10. Hollow steel tubes with an adjustable threaded stem on top, known as _____, enable columns to be adjusted as structures settle.

Section 6

Form Openings and Appendages

Unit 20   Form Openings

OBJECTIVES

After studying this unit, the student will be able to

- list types of form openings in concrete construction.
- differentiate between installation methods for wooden and metal opening forms.
- construct forms for openings.
- install opening forms in the wall forms.

Provisions must be made in concrete wall forms for openings for doors, windows, vents, utility items, and beam pockets. Forms for openings (also called *bucks*) are constructed after the wall units are in place. Opening forms are installed by nailing them in place between the two existing wall forms, figure 20-1. When the plastic concrete is placed

Fig. 20-1 Metal window buck in position between two wall forms.
Courtesy of Meyer Foundation Company, Incorporated

in the wall forms, it surrounds the opening forms, leaving the desired opening in the concrete wall. Opening forms must fit tightly so that the wet concrete does not leak around the form, thereby leaving a rough or uneven opening.

Great care should be exercised when determining the location of the openings. An opening out of position means extensive work to correct the problem; therefore, all measurements should be carefully checked before the opening form is nailed in place. Blueprints give the rough opening size and location. To accurately determine the location on the wall form, measure the specified distance from an established point, such as a corner or the top of a wall. Mark the position of the opening on the wall form. Double check all measurements for accuracy.

DOOR OPENINGS

Metal Doors

Doors used in residential structures are usually wooden; however, metal doors are sometimes used for basement doors. Metal doors are usually sold as a complete unit, including the metal door buck on which the door is eventually hung.

Installing Metal Door Bucks

1. Refer to the blueprints to find the size and location of the door. Rough dimensions for the door (the size before the door unit is installed) will also be found on the blueprints.
2. Measure and mark the door position on the concrete wall form.
3. Brace the metal door buck by placing boards the width of the door buck horizontally between the two sides of the buck, beginning at the bottom and working to the top at 2-foot intervals, figure 20-2. Bracing prevents

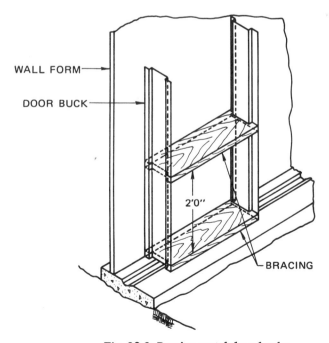

WALL FORM

DOOR BUCK

2'0"

BRACING

Fig. 20-2 Bracing metal door bucks.

the metal from buckling under the pressure of the wet concrete.

4. Set the metal door buck in position between the two concrete wall forms. Check the measurements to be sure they are correct.

5. Plumb both sides of the door buck and nail the buck to the wall forms. Nail from the outside of the forms, using double-headed nails for easier removal.

   Note: Some builders erect the outside wall form first and temporarily nail the door buck in place. The inside wall form is then set in place and secured. All measurements are checked to ensure that the door bucks are plumb and in the correct position before they are nailed securely to both wall forms.

6. Install two or three Number 5 reinforcement rods above the metal door buck for added structural strength. Reinforcement rods should extend 18 to 24 inches on each side of the frame, depending on the size of the door.

7. After all openings forms are securely nailed into position, pour the wet concrete. Consolidate the concrete as it is poured to eliminate any air pockets in the wall.

8. When the concrete has cured sufficiently, carefully strip the forms by first removing the nails which secure the opening forms. Strip the wall forms.

9. Remove the braces from the door buck which is now ready for installation of the door.

Doors Attached to a Wooden Frame

Most doors used in residential construction, including sliding glass doors, are attached to a wooden frame. Doors may be purchased as a complete unit with a preassembled door frame, or individual components may be purchased for assembly on the construction site. In either method, a wooden door buck must be constructed for the opening.

Door buck size is governed by the framing method used. One method involves using the door buck as the basic frame on which the door stop is nailed. Using this method, the inside dimensions for the door buck comprise the door size. If a preassembled unit is to be installed, the door buck will eventually be removed. The unit is nailed in place by nailing it to a nailing strip which is embedded in the concrete. If this method is used, the outside door buck dimensions coincide with the rough dimensions given on the blueprints. Typically, the concrete contractor constructs the opening form using one of these methods. The carpenter usually completes the framing if the opening is to be framed on site.

Installing Wooden Door Bucks

1. Read the blueprints for door specifications.

2. Measure and mark the door location on the wall form.

3. Cut 2-inch dimensional stock the width of the wall thickness. For example, a board 8 inches wide is used for 8-inch walls.

   A. If the door buck is to be used as the basic frame, cut one board the width of the door plus the thickness of the dimensional stock. For example, the board should be 33 inches for a 30-inch door.

   B. If the door buck is to be removed, cut one board the width of the rough opening.

4. Cut two boards for the sides.

   A. If the door buck is to be used as the basic frame, cut two boards the height of the door.

   B. If the door buck is to be removed, cut two boards the height of the rough opening minus the thickness of the top board.

5. Nail the door buck together to form the rough buck.

6. Nail a beveled 2-inch x 6-inch key in the center of the outside of the door buck, figure 20-3. The key serves as both a nailing strip if the buck is removed and as a device to lock the buck in place in the concrete.

   Note: If the door buck is to be removed, nail the key in place from the inside of the buck with duplex-head nails.

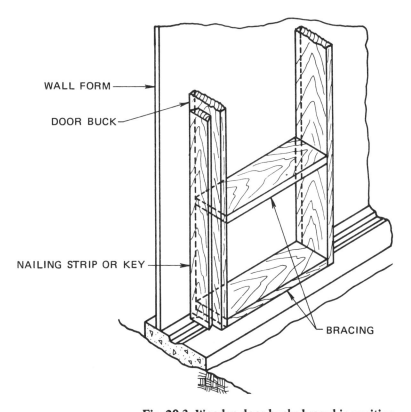

WALL FORM

DOOR BUCK

NAILING STRIP OR KEY

BRACING

Fig. 20-3 Wooden door bucks braced in position.

7. Brace the door buck with horizontal strips which measure the width of the buck. Place the first strip at the bottom and continue at 2-foot intervals. Bracing prevents the pressure of the wet concrete from pushing the door buck out of position.

   Note: If the door buck is to be removed, thoroughly oil the outside surface so that the concrete does not adhere to it. Do not oil the key.

8. Set the door buck in place between the wall forms.

9. Plumb both sides of the door buck and nail it to both wall forms. Use duplex-head nails for easy removal of the forms.

   Note: The door buck may be temporarily nailed to the outside wall form. The inside wall form is then positioned. Measurements and plumbness should be checked before the buck is securely nailed to both walls.

10. Place two or three Number 5 reinforcement rods above the door buck extending 18 to 24 inches on each side of the buck.

11. When all opening forms are secured, pour the wet concrete, consolidating it as it is poured to eliminate any air pockets in the wall.

12. After the concrete has cured, carefully strip the forms by first removing the nails which secure the opening forms. Strip the wall forms.

13. Remove the bracing and the door buck if it has been temporarily erected.

Fig. 20-4 Reusable vent buck in position on the outside wall form. Note the wire mesh which will remain in the wall after the forms are removed.
Courtesy of Proctor Products Company, Incorporated

WINDOW AND VENT OPENINGS

Metal Window Bucks and Vents

Basement window units may be wooden or metal. Metal windows and vents are sold as a complete unit with a metal buck which is set in the concrete wall form. Reusable vent bucks are available with wire mesh or a louvered vent which remains in the concrete after the forms and vent bucks are removed, figure 20-4, page 156.

1. Refer to the blueprints for the size and location of the openings.
2. Measure and mark the position of the window or vent on the wall forms.
3. Place the window or vent buck between the wall forms.
4. Plumb the metal buck and nail to both wall forms, using duplex-head nails which are nailed from the outside. As is the case with door bucks, window or vent bucks may be temporarily nailed to the outside wall first.

   Note: Bracing or reinforcement rods are rarely needed for window or vent bucks unless the opening is unusually large or far below the top of the wall.

5. When all forms are in place, pour wet concrete, consolidating it as it is poured to eliminate air pockets in the wall.
6. After the concrete has cured, remove all nails holding the opening forms. Strip the form walls.
7. Remove and clean the reusable vent bucks. Window bucks remain in place, ready for the window installation.

Figure 20-5 and figure 20-6, page 158, show the completed vent and the window frame after all forms have been removed.

Fig. 20-5 Vent unit with forms removed.
Courtesy of Meyer Foundation Company, Incorporated

Fig. 20-6 Window buck with forms removed.
Courtesy of Meyer Foundation Company, Incorporated

Fig. 20-7 Dryer vent buck. Notice the hinge on the top and the metal flange on the side.
Courtesy of Meyer Foundation Company, Incorporated

Note: Metal bucks can also be installed in a crawl space so that the window can be opened from the outside for access to utility connections.

Dryer vents are also available in units which can be installed in concrete forms, figure 20-7. A heavy gage, sheet metal buck fits over the dryer vent. The metal flange on the side of the buck in figure 20-7 locks the vent in the concrete. The vent buck is installed with the dryer vent in place and removed in two sections. Note the hinge on the top of the vent. After the wall forms are removed, the pin in the hinge is removed, after which each side of the vent buck is removed. The dryer vent remains locked in place by the metal flange. Separate inserts for vent bucks are available so that the buck may be used repeatedly.

Wooden Window Bucks

If wooden windows are specified, an opening form must be constructed of wood. As is the case with doors, the size of the window buck depends on whether the window buck is to be removed or if it is to be used as the basic frame. Because of the time involved in constructing a window frame, it is more economical to purchase complete window units; therefore, window frames are rarely built on site.

1. Read the blueprints for the rough opening size and window location.

2. Measure and mark the window opening on the wall form.

3. Cut 2-inch dimensional stock the thickness of the wall.

    A. If the window buck is to be removed, cut two boards equal to the width of the rough opening.

    B. If the window buck is to be used as the basic frame, cut two boards the width of the window, plus a 3-inch allowance for the end pieces.

4. Cut two boards for the sides.

    A. If the window buck is to be removed, the two boards are the height of the rough opening minus the 3-inch thickness of the top and bottom of the buck.

B.   If the window buck is to be used as the frame, the sides are the height of the window.

5. Nail the four boards together to form a rectangle.

    Note: Bracing for a window or vent buck is rarely needed because windows and vents are usually close to the top of the wall; therefore, the wet concrete exerts very little pressure on the buck.

6. Nail a beveled 2-inch x 6-inch key on the center of the outside of the buck. This locks the buck in place and serves as a nailing strip for the window frame if the buck is removed.

    Note: If the buck is to be removed, oil the outside surface thoroughly so that it does not adhere to the concrete. Do not oil the key.

7. Set the rough buck in place between the wall forms or on the outside wall.

8. Plumb the rough buck and nail it in position using duplex-head nails.

    Note: Reinforcement rods are not needed across the top unless the window or vent is placed well below the top of the wall.

9. Pour the wet concrete when all forms are tightly secured, consolidating it as it is poured.

10. Remove the duplex-head nails which hold the opening forms, strip the wall forms.

11. Remove the nails holding the window buck to the key. Pull the window buck from the opening. A slight tap with a hammer loosens the buck so that it slides out easily.

CAUTION: Never build a window buck and then attempt to purchase a window to fit. All window sizes should be determined in advance, and the manufacturer's rough opening sizes used in the construction specifications.

UTILITY OPENINGS

With advanced construction procedures and equipment such as high speed masonry drills, few utility openings are placed in the concrete wall form. Electrical wiring is usually installed through the wood framing of the house. Utility lines for water and the sewer usually enter under the footing and through the basement floor. The floor is placed around the utility lines after they are laid, figure 20-8, page 160.

If water or gas lines are installed through the wall, high speed masonry drills are used to drill through the concrete wall since the pipes for these utilities are usually 1 inch in diameter. This is the preferred method since it is quicker, more economical, and the hole can be drilled the exact size of the pipe. An exception occurs when a sewer pipe is being installed above the basement floor level. This requires an opening form which must be shaped out of sheet metal. A sheet metal form for a sewer pipe opening can be preformed when the sheet metal is purchased.

Fig. 20-8 Utility lines in place in a basement floor. Notice the reinforcement rods which hold the pipe in place until the basement floor is poured.

Courtesy of Mid-Missouri Company

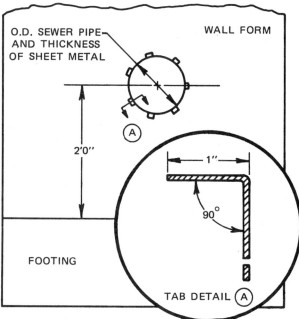

Fig. 20-9 Sheet metal sewer pipe form.

How to Form a Sewer Pipe Opening

1. Measure and mark the location of the sewer pipe opening on the wall forms.

2. Cut a strip of sheet metal the width of the wall plus approximately 2 inches for tabs on each end for fastening to the wall form. If the wall is 8 inches thick, the sheet metal should be long enough to fit around the pipe, plus a 1-inch allowance for overlapping.

3. Measure 1 inch on each side of the sheet metal strip and mark it by drawing a line all the way across the side of the strip.

4. Cut a series of tabs across each side by cutting to the 1-inch mark and folding the sheet metal tab to form a right angle, figure 20-9. The tabs will eventually be nailed to the wall form.

   CAUTION: Cut exactly 1 inch from the edge. The form must fit tightly against the wall form to prevent concrete leakage around the edge.

5. Form a circle to fit the sewer pipe and fasten the overlapping ends of the sheet metal with rivets.

6. Nail the form in position between the wall forms.

7. Pour the wet concrete after all forms are secured. Consolidate the concrete as it is poured.

8. When the concrete has cured, remove the forms. The metal tabs will show on the face of the wall; however, they may be cut off and the impressions covered with mortar when the holes from the tie breakbacks are filled.

Fig. 20-10 Steel girder resting in beam pocket.
Courtesy of Meyer Foundation Company, Incorporated

BEAM POCKETS

Beam pockets are indentations or box-like pockets along the inside top of walls in which primary beams or girders rest, figure 20-10. Beam pockets are also placed where beams are supported by pilasters. Forms for beam pockets may be purchased preformed for various size girders or constructed of wood.

The form for a beam pocket is a three-sided box open at the top and at one end. Beam pockets are the size of the outside dimensions of the form. The pocket should be large enough to leave approximately 1/2 inch on each side and end of the beam so that air is able to circulate. If a wooden girder or beam is used, the top of it should be level with the top of the sill plate. Therefore, the depth of the beam pocket is determined by the thickness of the girder plus the metal plate on which the girder rests. If a steel I-beam is used, the top of the beam is level with the top of the exterior wall.

How to Form a Beam Pocket

1. Refer to the blueprints for a girder size and location.

2. Measure along the inside wall forms and mark the location of each beam pocket.

   CAUTION: Beam pockets should be directly opposite each other on the inside of the exterior walls so that the girders are straight.

3. Cut the bottom board equal to the width and depth at which the beam will rest in the pocket, plus a 1/2-inch allowance in the back and a 1-inch allowance on the sides for air circulation.

4. Cut two side pieces equal to the height of the girder minus the thickness of the bottom board. The length should be equal to the depth at which the beam rests in the pocket, plus a 1/2-inch allowance for air circulation.

5. Cut the back side to fit between the two sides.

6. Nail the pieces together to form a three-sided box. It should be open at the top and at one end.

7. Thoroughly oil the exterior surface so that the form does not adhere to the concrete.

8. Using duplex-head nails, nail the form in position against the inside wall form.

CAUTION: There must be enough space between the beam pocket form and the outside wall form so that the beam is not exposed on the exterior.

9. When all forms are secured, pour the wet concrete, consolidating it as it is poured.

10. Remove the duplex-head nails which secure the beam pocket forms. Strip the wall forms.

11. After the wall forms are removed, remove the beam pocket forms by simply lifting them out.

APPLICATION

Complete each statement with the correct word or words.

1. All metal door bucks must be _____ to prevent buckling by the pressure of wet concrete.

2. For easy removal, _____ should be used to nail all opening forms to the wall forms.

3. Opening forms are nailed to the wall forms from the _____ of the wall form.

4. _____ should be installed across the top of the door buck to provide structural strength.

5. Metal vent bucks may be installed in a crawl space so that the window can be opened from the _____ for access to utility connections.

6. A 2-inch x 6-inch _____ is nailed around the center of the wood buck to lock it in place in the concrete and to serve as a nailing strip if the buck is removed.

7. _____ is the material used to make an opening form for a sewer pipe.

8. The form for a beam pocket is a three-sided box open in two places, at the _____ and _____ .

9. Beam pockets should be large enough to leave approximately _____ inch (inches) on each side and at the end of the girder for air circulation.

10. _____ are usually placed in position before basement floors are poured, with the basement floor poured around them.

Unit 21 Stair Forms

OBJECTIVES

After studying this unit, the student will be able to

- determine step rise and run.
- determine riser and tread width.
- list materials used in stair form construction.
- construct open and closed step forms.

Concrete steps are generally preferred for outside steps, since they last indefinitely and are not easily damaged. They are also safe and stable, with no structural weakness. Although prefabricated step forms and precast steps which can be set in place are available, most builders prefer to construct stair forms on site.

STAIR DESIGN

Exterior stairs may be either open or closed. Closed stairs may be built as an integral part of the entrance platform, figure 21-1. An expansion or isolation strip is placed between

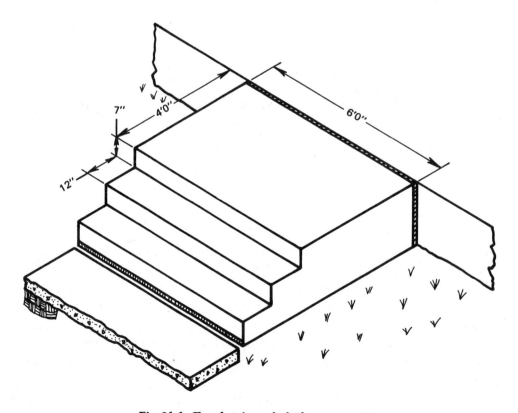

Fig. 21-1 Closed stairs and platform as a unit.

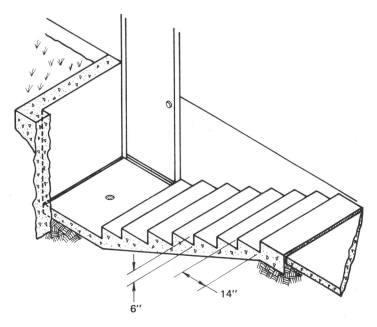

Fig. 21-2 Closed stairs positioned between two walls.

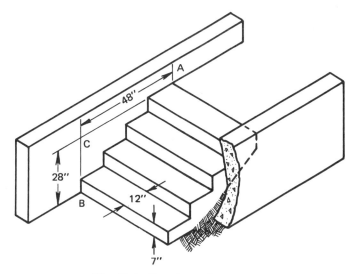

Fig. 21-3 Closed step layout.

the entrance platform and the foundation to prevent damage to the concrete. The possible damage is due to the fact that the soil may shift and settle differently under the entrance area because of the difference in the weight of the concrete, and because the entrance platform is poured above the frost line. The isolation strip also acts as a waterproofing seal.

Closed stairs may also be built between two existing walls, figure 21-2. Stairs of this type are usually built on sloping soil to conserve concrete. However, if the run is short, the soil may be leveled and the stairs poured to the ground level. This type of stairs is frequently used for exterior basement entrances.

Note: When constructing an outside basement entrance, a drain should always be placed at the base of the steps to prevent the accumulation of water.

Open stairs are supported at the top and bottom with an open space under the steps. Open stairs are more frequently constructed for interior stairs, although they may also be used for exterior stairs. Interior concrete stairs are rarely used for residential construction.

Whether concrete stairs are open or closed, the basic design for exterior stairs differs from that for interior stairs. On exterior steps, risers are lower and treads are wider to provide a safer surface when the stairs are wet or covered with snow or ice.

DETERMINING STEP RISE AND RUN

Before the forms for either closed or open stairs can be constructed, the step rise and run must be determined so that the riser height and tread width may be found. (The *rise* is the total height of the step; the *run* is the horizontal distance from the face of the first riser to the face of the last riser.) Figures 21-3, page 165 and 21-4 show layouts of concrete stairs. The measurements are used to determine the rise and run of the stairs. In figure 21-3, page 165, point A represents the upper sidewalk level; point B represents the lower sidewalk level. The distance from A to C represents the run or horizontal length of the stairs. The distance from B to C represents the rise.

The following steps may be used to determine stair rise and run.

1. For closed stairs between walls, mark a level line, starting at point A.

2. Mark a plumb line on the wall from point B until it intersects with the level line from point A. The intersection of the two lines establishes point C.

3. Measure the vertical distance between points B and C to obtain the total stair rise.

    A. For open stairs, measure from the top of the stairs or the entrance platform to the lower, or sidewalk, level.

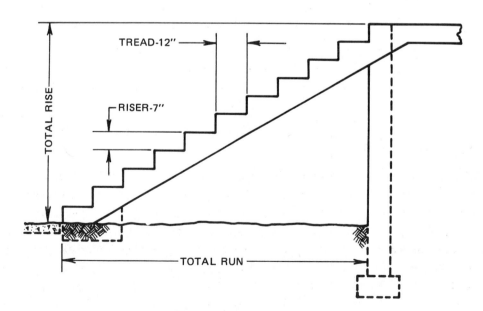

Fig. 21-4 Open stair layout.

4. Determine the number of risers by dividing the total riser height by 7 inches, the acceptable riser height for outside stairs. The result is the required number of risers. For example, if the total riser height from point B to C or from the sidewalk level to the top of the stairs is 28 inches, four 7-inch risers are required.

Note: If the total rise of the steps is not divisible by 7 inches, divide by an acceptable number to obtain both the height and number of risers. Risers should not measure over 7 inches; therefore, divide by a smaller number. For example, if the total rise of the stairs is 39 inches, divide 6.5 inches for six risers.

5. Determine the tread width.

A. If the total stair run is a definite length, simply divide the run by the number of risers. For the stairs in figure 21-3, page 165, divide the 48-inch run by four risers, which gives a 12-inch tread width.

Note: The length of a stair run is usually predetermined if the stairs are located between two walls or in a limited area. Otherwise, the length of the run is variable.

B. If the total stair run is variable, use the formula 2R + T = 26 inches to determine the tread width. In the formula, R is the riser height and T is the tread width. For example, if the riser height is 7 inches, 2 x 7 + T = 26 inches or 14 + T = 26 inches. Therefore, T = 26 inches – 14 inches, or T = 12 inches for a 12-inch tread width.

Note: Treads always number one less than the number of risers.

 CAUTION: Exterior stairs should be lower and wider than interior stairs to provide better footing in bad weather conditions. The maximum riser height for exterior stairs is usually 7 inches. The minimum tread width is usually 10 inches.

CLOSED STAIR FORMS

Closed stairs may be constructed between two existing walls, as part of the entrance platform, or directly on top of the soil. Although form design differs with each stair type, all forms should be constructed to provide a 4-inch concrete slab as a stair base.

When constructing forms for closed stairs between walls, figure 21-5, page 168, cleats or blocks are nailed to the hanging stringer along the layout marks for each tread and riser. Riser boards are then nailed to the blocks. The slope of the ground may be stepped or terraced so that the concrete does not slide. The soil should drain well so that water does not accumulate under the stairs. If the soil is a poorly draining soil such as clay, a well-tamped layer of gravel should be placed on top of the soil.

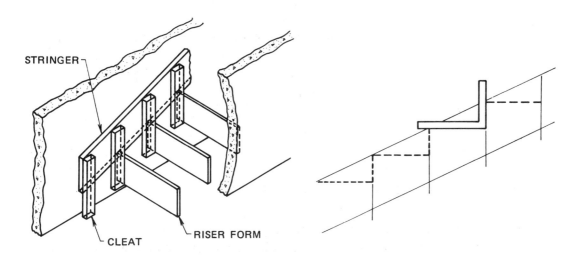

Fig. 21-5 Forms between two walls.   **Fig. 21-6 Stringer layout.**

How to Construct Closed Stair Forms Between Walls

1. Determine the number of risers, the riser height, and the tread width following the procedures listed on page 167.

2. Lay out the stringer using a carpenter's framing square. The stringer should be constructed of a 2-inch x 8-inch board. It should be long enough to stake at the bottom and fasten to the wood framing at the top. Lay the framing square on the stringer approximately one tread width from the end to provide space for the first cleat. Align the number on the tongue representing the riser height with the edge of the board. Align the number on the blade representing the tread width with the edge and mark the position of the step, figure 21-6. For example, if the riser measures 7 inches and the tread is 12 inches, align the number 7 on the tongue and the number 12 on the blade with the edge of the stringer. Continue this procedure until all the risers have been marked. Extend the last tread line to the back edge of the stringer. There should be enough room on the end to stake the stringer.

3. Nail the cleats or blocks in position. The cleats hold the riser boards in place. Place each cleat 1 1/2 inches from the riser mark so that there is room to nail the riser board to the cleat. Plumb the cleat and nail it in place. Continue until there is a cleat for each riser board.

   Note: There should be an approximate 1/2-inch allowance between the bottom of the cleat and the tread. This allows enough space to trowel the entire tread surface.

4. Set the stringers in position on each side by driving a 2-inch x 4-inch stake 24 inches long solidly in the ground and nailing it to the stringer.

⭐ **CAUTION:** The stake should be as close to the wall as possible.

5. Cut the required number of riser forms from 2-inch stock. Each form should be equal to the riser height and width. For example, if the steps are 36 inches wide and each riser is 7 inches high, each form should be 7 inches wide and 36 inches long. Riser forms should be beveled so that the face of the tread can be troweled to the face of the riser while the concrete is wet and the forms are in place.

   Note: Most riser forms are straight boards with a beveled edge at the bottom, figure 21-7(A); however, other forms may be used. A sloped riser which provides a wider tread may be constructed using a straight tilted form, figure 21-7(B). If this type of form is used, the cleats should be placed so that the riser forms can be nailed at the correct angle.

6. Nailing from the inside with 8d nails, nail the riser forms to the cleats. Each riser form should be aligned with the riser layout on the stringer. Check the level of the riser board by placing a spirit level along the top edge of the riser board.

   Note: Oil the riser forms for easy removal.

7. Pour a layer of concrete approximately 2 inches thick. Air-entrained concrete is the best mix for flat areas exposed to weather and other forces.

   Note: If the soil is dry, moisten the area so that it does not absorb water from the concrete. The ground, however, should not be muddy.

8. Place Number 4 reinforcing rods approximately 9 inches apart, beginning 3 inches from the wall.

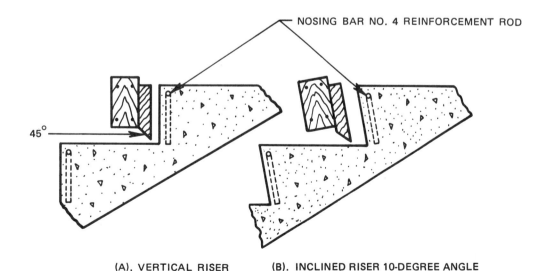

NOSING BAR NO. 4 REINFORCEMENT ROD

45°

(A). VERTICAL RISER   (B). INCLINED RISER 10-DEGREE ANGLE

Fig. 21-7 Stair treads and nosing.

9. Pour the concrete for the rest of the steps.

   Note: If the steps are unusually wide, the riser fronts may be braced to prevent them from bulging from the pressure of the wet concrete.

10. Place a riser nosing bar which is bent 90 degrees on each end near the front of each tread so that it is surrounded by approximately 1 inch of concrete.

11. Trowel the wet concrete surface until the desired finish is obtained.

12. After the concrete has cured, remove the forms.

How to Construct an Entrance Platform with Closed Steps

If the entrance platform is relatively small and there are only two or three stairs, the entrance area and the stairs are usually poured as one unit, figure 21-8. A well-tamped layer of gravel under the entrance platform and stairs provides adequate drainage so that water does not accumulate underneath the area.

1. Read the blueprints for the platform size. Determine the number of risers, riser height, and tread width.

2. Cut two 2-inch boards the width of the riser height and equal in length to the depth of the entrance platform. For example, if the rise is 7 inches high and the entrance platform is 4 feet from the foundation to the first riser, the boards should measure 7 inches wide and 4 feet long.

3. Cut two 2-inch boards the width of the riser height and equal in length to the depth of the entrance platfotm plus the tread width. Continue this procedure until there are two boards for each riser.

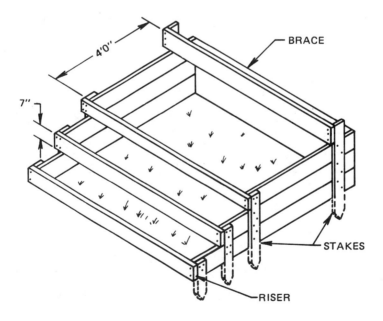

Fig. 21-8 Entrance platform and stair forms.

4. Cut six or eight stakes from 2 inch x 4 inch stock. Each stake should be long enough to nail the forms together with 1 foot on the bottom for driving it into the ground and a 6-inch allowance on the top for a brace.

5. Measure the area for the platform and stairs. Add 1 1/2 inches on each side for the stakes. Drive the stakes firmly into the ground, with the first stake 6 to 8 inches from the structure and the others approximately every 18 inches apart.

6. Nail the form boards to the stakes using 8d nails.

CAUTION: Check to be sure the forms are plumb and level before they are nailed securely.

7. Place an expansion joint or isolation strip of 1/2-inch asphaltum-saturated felt between the form and the foundation. The sticky surface of the mixture adheres to the foundation. If the entrance area is attached to the foundation, freezing, expanding, and contracting soil may damage the foundation.

   Note: All entrance areas are poured over a buttress which is a part of the foundation. The buttress relieves some of the pressure exerted on the foundation.

8. Cut the required number of riser forms from 2-inch stock equal in width to the riser height and equal in length to the step width, plus a 3-inch allowance for nailing. For example, if the risers are 7 inches high and the steps are 42 inches wide, the boards should be 7 inches wide and 45 inches long.

   Note: Riser forms should be beveled on one edge so that the tread can be troweled to the riser face. Riser forms may be angled to provide a wider tread as discussed earlier.

9. Nail the riser forms to the side forms. Oil both the side and riser forms for easy removal.

10. Cut braces for each pair of stakes. The braces should be long enough to reach across the forms and be nailed to the stakes.

11. Place the concrete, consolidating it as it is poured to prevent air spaces. Concrete which is 6 percent air-entrained should be used.

    Note: If the steps are unusually wide, the riser boards may be braced to prevent bulging from the wet concrete.

12. Place a riser nosing bar on each end near the front of the treads so that 1 inch of concrete surrounds the bar.

    Note: Nosing bars are strips of metal placed across the edge of stair treads. They are the only reinforcement needed for this type of step.

13. Trowel the surface until the designed finish is obtained.

14. After the concrete has cured, remove the forms.

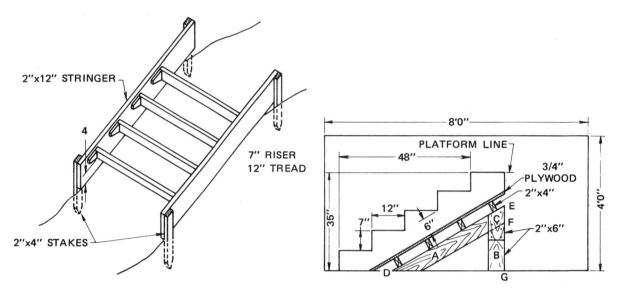

Fig. 21-9 Closed stair forms on a slope.

Fig. 21-10 Open step layout.

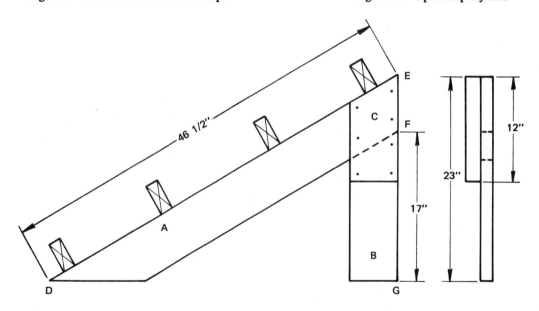

Fig 21-11 Support horses and cross joists of open step form.

Forms for closed stairs which are built on top of a sloped area are constructed essentially the same as open stair forms. The stringer for the closed stairs must be wide enough to fit against the slope and provide for a 4-inch slab under the stairs, figure.21-9. No platform is needed to support the top of closed stair forms.

OPEN STAIR FORMS

While following the steps in the construction of an open step stair, refer to figure 21-10.

1. Determine the number of risers, riser height, and the full size of the tread width following the procedure discussed on page 170.

2. Lay out the stair form on the plywood sheet.

3. Construct the platform as shown in figure 21-11, page 172.

    A. Cut two boards to support the soffit. The boards should be cut from 2 inch x 6 inch material. Each board should be the length of the incline from point D to point E in figure 21-10, page 172. The length of the incline and bevel is determined from the full scale drawing on the plywood sheet. After they are cut, lay the boards on the layout to be sure that they fit.

    B. Cut two boards (B in figure 21-10, page 172) from 2 inch x 6 inch material to vertically support the top of the form. These boards must be long enough to hold the top tread even with the platform line in figure 21-10, page 172. To obtain the length, measure the distance on the layout from point F to point G. Lay the board on the layout drawing to be sure that it fits.

    C. Cut four boards (C in figure 21-10, page 172) to nail the supporting horses together.

    D. Nail the supporting horses securely together.

    E. Cut the required number of supporting cross joists from 2-inch x 4-inch material. Each cross joist is equal in length to the width of the plywood sheet.

    F. Place the supporting horses the required distance apart. Position them underneath the stringers.

    G. Place the cross joists on edge and nail them to the inclined tops of the supporting horses. The joists should be spaced approximately 16 inches O.C. This completes the supporting platform.

4. Lay out the stringer on a 2-inch x 12-inch board by use of a framing square. Place the stringer on a sawhorse. Align the number representing the riser height on the tongue of the framing square and the number representing the tread width on the blade of the framing square. Move the square and repeat the process until the required number of risers and treads have been drawn. Extend the last tread line to the back edge of the stringer. Extend the last tread and riser line to the back edge at the top of the stringer.

5. Cut the stringer with a cross cut saw. The stringers should fit closely to the layout on the plywood sheet.

6. Measure the step width on a sheet of plywood and make a mark. The plywood sheet should be wide enough to extend approximately 3 inches on each side of the stringers to provide room for nailing it to the platform. For example, if the stairs are 36 inches wide, a 3-inch allowance should be made for the stringers in addition to a 6-inch allowance for the extension on each side; therefore, the plywood sheet

should be 45 inches wide. The length should correspond to the length of the stringer incline from point A to B in figure 21-12.

Note: Use the plywood sheet on which the layout was made.

7. Place the stringers along the outside edge of the marks and nail them securely in place with duplex-head nails.

8. Place the supporting horses against the wall where the stairs are to be poured. To help prevent the horses from slipping, brace them by driving a stake against the supporting legs so that the horses are positioned between the wall and the stake.

9. Place the stringer and soffit on the supporting horses. Check the plumb and total rise. Nail the stair form securely to the supporting horses. When nailing the stair form, use double-headed nails. Nail through the extended plywood to the cross joists.

10. Cut the required number of riser boards from 2-inch material. Be sure that it is the specified length and width. For example, for a 7-inch rise and a 36-inch stair, cut the riser boards 7 inches wide and 39 inches long. This gives a 1 1/2-inch allowance on each end so that they can be nailed to the stringer.

    Note: The bottom of all riser boards except the bottom riser should be beveled to the riser face. As previously mentioned, the riser forms may be angled.

11. Nail the riser boards securely to the stringer using duplex-head nails. Check the level of the riser by placing a level along its top. The form is now complete, figure 21-12.

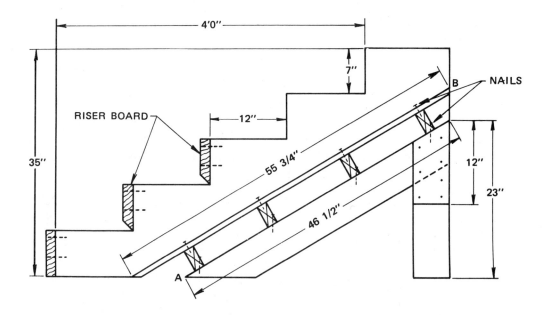

Fig. 21-12 Complete open stair form.

Note: The surface of the form should be oiled for easy removal.

12. Pour a 2-inch layer of 6-percent air-entrained concrete.

13. Place Number 4 reinforcement rods approximately 9 inches apart beginning 3 inches from the wall. Open steps are not supported as closed stairs are; therefore, reinforcement rods should extend beyond the top of the steps to tie the steps to the upper platform.

14. Pour the remaining concrete, consolidating it as it is poured to eliminate air pockets.

    Note: If the steps are unusually wide, the riser boards may be braced.

15. Place a riser nosing bar which is bent at a 90-degree angle on each end near the front of each tread so that the nosing bar is surrounded with approximately 1 inch of concrete.

16. Trowel the tread surface to the desired finish.

17. After the concrete has cured sufficiently, carefully remove the forms.

APPLICATION

Complete each statement with the correct word or words.

1. Exterior steps should be _____ and _____ than interior steps to provide better footing in bad weather conditions.

2. The number of 7-inch risers needed for stairs with a total rise of 35 inches is _____.

3. The tread width for stairs with a 60-inch run and five risers is _____ inches.

4. To determine the tread width for a variable run, use the formula _____.

5. _____ _____ are stairs built directly on top of the ground.

6. When laying out a stringer, the number on the tongue of the framing square represents the _____.

7. There should be a _____-inch slab under the stairs whether they are open or closed.

8. Riser boards should be _____ at the bottom so that the tread can be troweled to the face of the riser.

9. _____ should be placed near the front of each tread and covered with approximately 1 inch of concrete.

10. When building open stair forms, a full scale layout should be drawn on the _____ which is used for the soffit.

Unit 22 Entrance Platforms and Patios

OBJECTIVES

After studying this unit, the student will be able to

- assemble prefabricated buttress or stoop forms.
- construct concrete forms for entrance platforms.
- construct patio forms.

Residential contractors frequently contract for a total foundation job which includes the basic foundation, the entrance platform, exterior steps, and a patio. They may also contract for individual exterior jobs in one of these areas for a structure which is already completed.

THE BUTTRESS FORM

A *buttress*, figure 22-1, is a structure built against a building to give it greater stability. A sloped buttress may be used to support and distribute the weight of the entrance platform or stoop. Buttresses may be poured as part of the foundation wall with prefabricated forms, figure 22-2, page 177.

Fig. 22-1 Concrete buttress lending support to an entrance platform.
Courtesy of Mid-Missouri Company

Constructing a Buttress

1. Refer to the blueprints for the entrance location.

2. Locate the buttress position on the exterior wall by measuring from a given point, such as the corner of the wall. Each buttress should be positioned so that the edge of the entrance platform rests on it.

   Note: The top of the buttress should be level with the grade line.

3. Attach the oiled buttress forms to the wall forms following the procedures below.

   A. Each buttress form is available in two sections. Place one side in position and fasten it to the wall form with the forming hardware.

   B. Place the second section in position and fasten it to the wall form.

   C. Fasten the two buttress forms together with the forming hardware.

   Note: Usually, only two buttress forms are required. However, if the entrance platform is unusually wide, another form may be placed under the center of the entrance platform.

4. Pour the buttress as part of the foundation wall.

   Note: Always consolidate the concrete as it is being poured to eliminate air pockets.

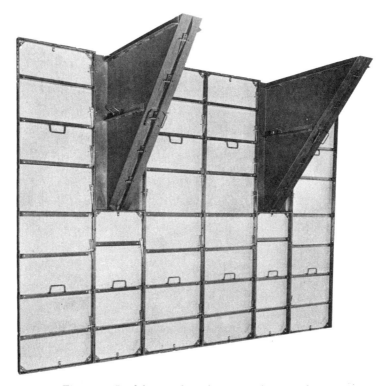

Fig. 22-2 Prefabricated steel stoop or buttress form.
Courtesy of Symons Corporation

5. After the concrete has cured sufficiently, the buttress forms are removed by simply unfastening the form hardware and lifting the forms away from the concrete.

ENTRANCE PLATFORMS

The height of an entrance platform is determined by the structural design, the foundation height, and the grade line. A simple concrete slab poured directly on top of the buttress is the type of platform most frequently used in modern residential construction. The slab may be from 4 to 8 inches thick. Other platforms include a platform which is built up and consists of three walls and a slab top, and the solid platform with steps.

Construction of the Slab Platform

1. Read the blueprints to determine the platform size and location.

2. Fill the open area around the foundation and the buttress with soil from the basement excavation. Tamp the soil thoroughly with a tamper. If the soil does not drain well, place a layer of gravel between the buttress forms.

   Note: The fill should be level with the top of the buttress; it should not cover the buttress.

3. Using 2-inch stock, cut three boards the required width and length for forms. For example, if the entrance platform is to be 4 feet x 6 feet and 6 inches thick, cut two boards 4 feet long and 6 inches wide. Cut one board 6 feet 3 inches long and 6 inches wide.

   Note: The 3-inch allowance on the 6-foot board is to leave space in which to nail the forms together.

4. Cut the required number of stakes. The stakes should be cut from 2-inch x 4-inch material 18 to 24 inches long and tapered on the end.

5. Make the proper measurements to determine the platform location.

   Note: Entrance platforms should be centered on the buttress to evenly distribute the weight.

6. Drive the stakes in the ground at the platform edge, leaving a 1 1/2-inch allowance for the form boards. Stakes prevent the forms from bulging under the pressure of the wet concrete.

7. Connect the three boards and nail them to the stakes as shown in figure 22-3, page 179.

   Note: The inside of the boards should be oiled for easy removal.

8. Check the forms to be sure that they are level and that the corners are square.

9. Place a 1/2-inch thick expansion joint of asphaltum-saturated felt along the foundation surface. The expansion joint is necessary since the entrance slab is above the frost line and is subject to heaving. The expansion

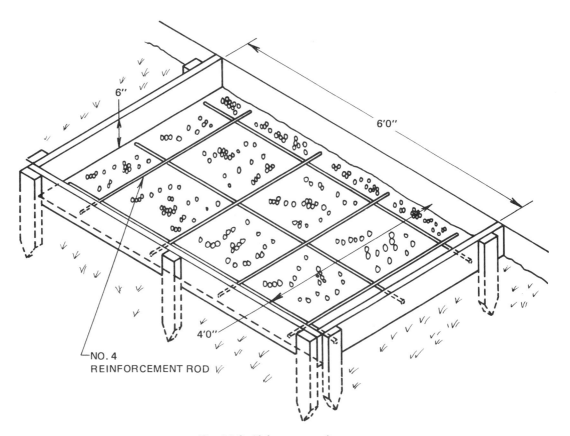

6"

6'0"

4'0"

NO. 4
REINFORCEMENT ROD

Fig. 22-3 Slab entrance form.

joint separates the entrance platform from the foundation, thus lessening strain on the foundation which might result in cracks in the
foundation wall. The expansion joint also serves as a waterproof seal.

10. Pour a 2-inch layer of concrete. Concrete which is 6-percent air-entrained should be used for flat exterior surfaces exposed to bad weather
conditions and other forces.

11. Construct a grid in the shape of 18-inch squares with Number 4 reinforcement rods.

12. Pour the remaining concrete over the grid, consolidating it as it is
poured.

    Note: Concrete on a flat, exposed surface should be cured slowly to
    prevent fine surface cracks. This may be accomplished by keeping the
    concrete damp, either by sprinkling it daily with water or by placing a
    damp burlap cover over the surface. Admixtures may also be added to
    the concrete to retard curing. Slow curing should take three days.

13. Trowel the top of the slab until the desired finish is obtained.

14. After the concrete has cured, remove the forms.

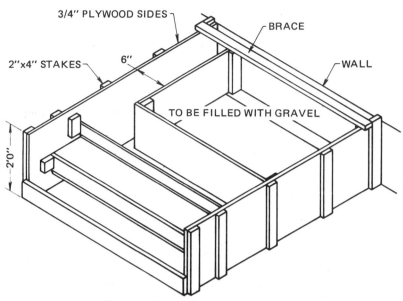

3/4" PLYWOOD SIDES
BRACE
2"x4" STAKES
6"
WALL
TO BE FILLED WITH GRAVEL
2'0"

Fig. 22-4 Forms for entrance platform.

Construction of the Built-Up Entrance Platform

1. Refer to the blueprints for the platform size.

2. Measure to determine the platform location. Stake the platform building lines by stretching a line from stake to stake.

3. Using 2-inch x 4-inch stock, cut stakes, braces, and ties, figure 22-4.

4. Nail studs to the wall forms at 2-foot intervals. Use either small prefabricated panels or 3/4-inch plywood.

5. Drive the stakes in the ground at 2-foot intervals so that they are even with the studs on the forms.

6. Set the oiled forms in place and nail the braces to the stakes and studs. Fasten the top together with ties. The forms should fit tightly against the wall.

    Note: A 6-inch wall is sufficient for an entrance platform.

7. Check the forms to ensure that they are level and that the corners are square. Remove the building lines and stakes.

8. Measure the height of the entrance platform. Snap a chalk line along the face of the outside wall form to indicate the platform height. Snap another chalk line 4 inches below to indicate the top of the wall.

9. Place a 1/2–inch thick expansion joint along the foundation wall at the point at which the walls meet.

10. Pour concrete to the first chalk mark which designates the top of the wall. Curing precautions should be observed as discussed above.

    Note: Consolidate the concrete as it is being poured.

11. After the concrete has cured, remove the inside wall form.

12. Fill the rectangular area to the top of the wall with coarse gravel. Tamp the gravel thoroughly with a tamper.

13. Pour a 2-inch layer of 6-percent air-entrained concrete on top of the gravel and the wall.

14. Form a grid of 18-inch squares on the concrete using Number 4 reinforcement rods.

15. Place the remaining concrete to the level indicated on the outside wall form.

16. Trowel the surface until the desired finish is obtained.

17. After the concrete has cured, remove the outside wall forms.

THE CONCRETE PATIO

1. Determine the location, size, and shape of the patio.

2. Stake the patio area and stretch form lines using string stretched from stake to stake.

3. Excavate the entire patio area 4 to 6 inches.

   Note: The excavation depth is determined by the soil type. If the soil is sandy and drains well, the patio can be poured directly on top of the soil; therefore, the area should be excavated to a 4-inch depth. If the soil is a clay or clay-mixed soil and does not drain well, a 2-inch layer of crushed stone should be placed in the excavated area with the patio poured on top of the crushed stone; therefore, the area should be excavated to a 6-inch depth.

4. Compact the soil with a tamper and place the crushed stone, if required, in the excavated area. Thoroughly compact the gravel with a tamper.

5. Cut 2-inch x 4-inch boards the required size to form the patio forms.

   Note: Patio forms can be built in almost any shape if 1/4-inch plywood is used for the forms. Plywood can be easily curved to form various designs. If a curved form of plywood is used, stakes should be placed at 12-inch intervals around the curved areas.

6. Cut 12-inch stakes tapered on one end from 1-inch x 4-inch stock.

7. Drive the stakes into the ground, spacing them approximately 4 feet apart unless the design requires closer spacing as discussed above. The stakes should be placed 1 1/2 inches outside the form lines to allow space for the forms.

8. Nail the forms to the stakes, sloping toward one end. The forms should slope approximately 1/8 inch per foot toward one end of the patio to provide for adequate drainage. For example, the total slope for a 12-foot patio is 1 1/2 inches.

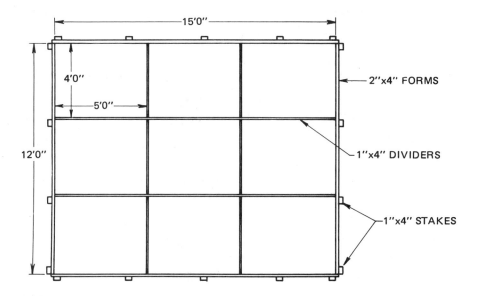

Fig. 22-5 Patio form with dividers.

Note: A 1/2-inch isolation strip and waterproof seal should be placed between the patio and existing concrete surfaces such as the foundation or sidewalk.

9. Place Number 10 wire mesh on the ground surface.

10. If the area of the patio is larger than 10 feet x 10 feet, expansion joints must be provided to prevent the concrete from cracking and shifting the soil.

  A. Toenail dividers cut from 1-inch x 4-inch material in place, figure 22-5. (To *toenail* is to drive a nail into the end of a piece of lumber at a slanting angle to join it to another piece of lumber.) Decorative dividers can be constructed from various wood such as redwood or cedar.

  B. Form joints with a groover while the concrete is wet.

  C. Joints may be cut with a masonry saw after the concrete has cured one day.

11. Dampen the excavated area or gravel fill with a hose before pouring the concrete. If the ground absorbs water, thereby causing the concrete to cure too rapidly, fine surface cracks may result.

12. Pour 6-percent air-entrained concrete the full depth of the patio. The amount of concrete needed for a patio can be estimated by using the following formula.

$$\frac{\text{thickness (in feet) x width (in feet) x length (in feet)}}{27} = \text{cubic yards}$$

After applying the formula, add a 5- to 10-percent allowance for waste. For example, if the patio measures 12 feet x 15 feet, apply the original formula:

$$\frac{1/3 \times 12 \times 15}{27} = 2.2 \text{ cubic yards}$$

Add .2 yard for waste. The total amount of concrete needed is 2.4 cubic yards. Round off the figure to 2 1/2 cubic yards when ordering.

13. Screed the concrete surface using a straight 2-inch x 4-inch board drawn across the top of the concrete to level it. Color can be added at this point by sprinkling a powdered dye over the surface before it is floated.

14. Float the wet concrete using a metal float. Place a board on the wet concrete to kneel on while floating the concrete. Work the float in an up and down motion then smooth the area. Continue this process until the entire area has been floated.

15. Finish the concrete as desired. Numerous decorative finishes can be obtained.

    A. The surface can be troweled to a smooth finish, or designs can be troweled.

    B. A stiff-bristled brush can be drawn across the surface to obtain a brush surface.

    C. A groover can be used to place decorative designs or expansion joints.

    D. A rough aggregate can be scattered over the surface to provide an appearance of stone.

16. Allow the concrete to cure slowly, keeping it damp to obtain a surface finish free of defects. Remove the forms after the concrete has cured.

APPLICATION

Complete each statement with the correct word or words.

1. A (an) _____ is constructed on an outside wall where greater than normal pressure is to be exerted.

2. The top of buttresses should be level with the _____.

3. The soil under entrance platforms should be well _____.

4. A (An) _____ should always be placed between entrance platforms and the foundations.

5. Concrete which is _____ percent air-entrained should be used for flat exterior surfaces exposed to harsh weather conditions and other forces.

6. A grid constructed of _____ should be placed in entrance platforms.

7. Patio areas should be excavated to a (an) _____ – to _____-inch depth.

8. Patio forms should slope toward one end at the rate of approximately _____ per foot.

9. A straight board measuring 2 inches x 4 inches should be used to _____ the patio surface after it is poured.

10. A (An) _____ may be used to place decorative designs or expansion joints in wet concrete.

Unit 23   Swimming Pool Construction

OBJECTIVES

After studying this unit, the student will be able to

- list differences between construction procedures for concrete pools and fiber glass and concrete pools.
- list the basic construction procedures for a swimming pool.

Swimming pools are becoming an increasingly popular item in residential communities across the country. At one time, swimming pools built below grade were almost always concrete. Concrete pools remain popular; however, pools built with less costly materials are becoming more common.

Concrete pools are poured in much the same way as foundations are. Forms are erected in the desired shape and inserts are installed for the circulating and drainage system. The concrete is then poured around reinforcement rods. The filter and ladder are attached after the forms are removed.

One of the more popular pools which makes use of materials other than concrete is the combination fiber glass and concrete pool. This pool is built from a kit which includes a detailed instruction booklet with a tools list, a materials list, and step-by-step construction procedures.

When building any pool, it is imperative that the contractor follow the detailed instructions that come with each pool kit.

CONSTRUCTION OF THE FIBERGLASS AND CONCRETE POOL

The following illustrations are on-site construction photographs used to provide a graphic description of the operations involved in pool construction. The pool shown is a kidney-shaped pool manufactured by Hallmark Pool Corporation. The pool was constructed on a sloped site between a house and a retaining wall. When the pool was completed, the area was filled and a pool deck and patio were poured.

Fiberglass and concrete pools are constructed in a variety of shapes including the kidney, palatte, oval, L-shaped, and rectangular. The rounded shapes such as the kidney are easier to shape than the rectangular since they require less total form work.

Pool Location

Several factors should be considered before the final pool location is determined.

1. The pool area should drain well. If the soil drains well, the pool can be installed with no problems; however, a layer of well-tamped crushed stone should be placed on the floor of the pool. If the desired location is in an area which does not drain well, a perimeter drainage system may be required. The perimeter drainage system acts to carry water away from the pool so that it does not accumulate underneath and weaken the pool structure.

2. Be sure that the grade line at the pool edge is above the surrounding area so that surface water from the surrounding area drains away from the pool.

3. Clear the area of utility lines. Utility lines can usually be routed around the pool area; this, however, can be a very expensive procedure.

4. Check local zoning regulations to determine the minimum setback and fencing regulations. All pools must be adequately fenced.

5. Be sure that the pool is located so that it receives maximum sunlight.

Pool Layout

The first step in the construction of a pool is laying it out. Rectangular pools are simply measured from a reference point and staked. A 20-inch allowance is made around the pool for excavation.

Other forms are more difficult to lay out. The instruction booklet in each pool kit shows an illustration with a pool layout and specific measurements for laying out and staking the pool. Since layout instructions vary with different pools, they should be carefully followed.

Pool Excavation

Excavation is one of the most critical steps in pool construction. Again, each instruction booklet shows an excavation layout giving specific depths at each point. There are, however, a few general statements which apply to all pools.

The excavated area is 20 inches larger on all sides than the actual pool. A builder's transit is used to control the depth at various points. The depth should be frequently checked as the excavation progresses. The excavation along the perimeter should be equal in depth to the pool wall height. The deep end of the pool should have an 18-inch ledge which gradually slopes toward the deeper area. The depth and slope of the remainder of the pool is determined from the pool layout in the instruction booklet. The excavation should be smooth and hand trimmed, if necessary, to maintain a uniform concrete thickness and avoid unnecesary waste of materials.

Pool Construction

1. Place the main drain in the excavated area so that it is level with the finished surface. Connect a 1 1/2-inch drainpipe to the drain and lay it on the floor. The drainpipe leads to either the skimmer line or the circulating pump, depending on the system being used. Cover the pipe with gravel or sand so that it does not shift when the pool is packed.

    Note: Stuff the main drain with cloth and tape it closed until the finish coat has been applied.

    CAUTION: It is imperative that the connections be watertight.

2. Cover the entire floor area with Number 10 wire reinforcing mesh. Place the mesh directly on the pool floor and cut it to the shape of the pool. The mesh should be overlapped 6 inches at each joint and wired

Fig. 23-1 Pool jack holding panels upright. Notice the vinyl coping across the top and the reinforcement rods extending from the panels into the ground.

Courtesy of Meyer Foundation Company, Incorporated

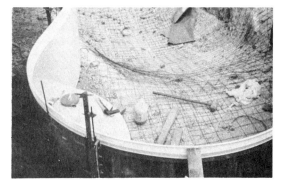

Fig. 23-2 Pool shell ready for floor installation. Notice the placement of the drain, drainpipe, and wire mesh.

Courtesy of Meyer Foundation Company, Incorporated

together. As the concrete is packed, the mesh is pulled up so that it is suspended in the concrete.

3. Assemble the side panels in sections of three. The flanges of each panel should be thoroughly coated with butyl caulk and then bolted together. Set the panels in place.

4. Set *pool jacks* (metal fence posts equipped with a hanger) at each seam where the three assembled panels meet. The pool jacks are bolted to the metal flange on the panels to hold them upright, figure 23-1. As each assembled section is placed, the flanges are caulked and bolted. This process is continued until all of the panels are in place. The steps are placed as part of the panels. The top of the panels should be 3 to 4 inches above the ground level.

   Note: As the panels are set in place, a builder's transit is used to level the pool wall.

5. Install the vinyl coping. Joints should meet at either a straight area or on a slight curve. A 7-inch insert is used to join and match one vinyl section with another.

6. Drive Number 3 reinforcement rods in the ground to the desired depth. Place each reinforcement rod in the tube on the back of the panels.. Place a second rod on top of the first and use it to drive the first rod to the desired depth. Remove the second rod. Continue this procedure until there is a reinforcement rod in each tube.

7. After the wall jacks, vinyl coping, and reinforcement rods are in place, check to be sure that the wall is level. If the soil is sandy or loose, it may be necessary to place a temporary block under the pool wall so that it remains level. Figure 23-2 shows the pool with the mesh and wall installed.

8. Following the instructions in the booklet, install light niches, skimmers, and water insets. These accessories should be embedded in the

Fig. 23-3 Water inlet.

Courtesy of Meyer Foundation Company, Incorporated

Fig. 23-4 Reinforcement rods ready to be embedded in the soil. Notice placement of the skimmers and drainpipe.

Courtesy of Meyer Foundation Company, Incorporated

concrete so that shifting soil cannot displace them. Figure 23-3 shows the water inlet before concrete has been placed around it. Figure 23-4 shows the reinforcement rods, skimmers, and drainpipe.

9. Install the grounding system. All metal must be grounded to guard against potential electrical shocks. The grounding system must meet the specifications of the National Electrical Code which are given in the instruction booklet. If the contractor is not a qualified electrician, an electrician should install the grounding system. An electrician should also be responsible for wiring and grounding the lights and skimmer.

10. Bend 4 1/2-foot Number 3 reinforcement rods at a 90-degree angle approximately 1 foot from one end and 1 1/4 feet from the other end. Place the short end in the tube on the back of the panel. Embed the other end in the ground. Continue this procedure until there is a reinforcement rod in each tube. Notice the placement of the reinforcement rods in figure 23-4. Because of the location of the pool, the reinforcement rods are tied to the retaining wall instead of being embedded in the ground.

11. Pack the pool floor. (Concrete is *packed* rather than placed or poured when a very dry mixture is being used, as opposed to the wet mixture used for sidewalks.) All tools and equipment must be ready before the floor is placed. The concrete must be the correct mix. Concrete specifications given in the instruction booklet should be carefully followed. The ideal time to pack the floor is in the morning so that the sun does not dry the mix too rapidly. The pool area should be moist; however, there should be no standing water.

A. Place a rim of concrete around the outside of the panels for the footing. Start at the outside edge and slowly work out against the panels to at least a 6-inch depth above the lower edge of the panel. Place approximately 24 feet of area.

Fig. 23-5 Deck and patio area ready to be poured. The grid consists of Number 4 reinforcement rods.

Courtesy of Meyer Foundation Company, Incorporated

Fig. 23-6 Finished pool deck and patio with scoring. Notice the skimmer top which can be removed for cleaning.

Courtesy of Meyer Foundation Company, Incorporated

B. Pack concrete in the center of the deepest area and work toward the area completed in Step A. There must be at least two people to pack the concrete. One person turns the concrete over with a shovel and distributes it to a 6-inch minimum depth. A finisher floats the concrete to the desired finish. The area is broom-finished as it begins to dry so that a rough surface results. Check the level of the pool wall at the completion of each packing operation. If the wall is not level, make the required adjustments to level it. This process is continued until the entire area is covered.

CAUTION: Be sure to pull the wire mesh up to the correct level 2 to 3 inches from the bottom so that it is suspended in the center of the concrete.

C. Repeat Steps A and B. Begin with the footing around the edge and move to the center of the remaining pool area, working to the edge.

Note: Always start at the deepest end and work toward the shallow end.

12. Pour a 3-foot x 7-inch slab for the filter system.

13. When the slab is dry, install the filter system. Follow instructions in the installation booklet.

14. Carefully remove the pool jacks as soon as the concrete is solid enough to support the wall sections.

15. Install ladder anchors and safety line fastening hardware, following the booklet instructions.

16. Place the tile around the edge of the pool. Apply mastic adhesive to the top inside pool wall with a toothed trowel and a putty knife. Press the tile into the mastic. Complete a small area at a time. Grout the face of the tile with waterproof grout. Be sure to clean all mastic and grout from the face of the tile while it is wet.

Fig. 23-7 Diving board and ladder in place.
Courtesy of Meyer Foundation Company, Incorporated

17. Backfill the area by hand with washed gravel. If a large volume of backfill is placed mechanically, the pool walls may be shifted. Do not tamp the backfill. It should, however, be evenly distributed.

18. Check the walls to be sure they are plumb as the backfilling is done.

19. Construct the forms for the pool deck, following the procedures given for patio construction. The pool deck should be at least 3 feet wide. Forms should be 3/4 inch below the vinyl coping so that the back splash from the pool drains properly. Tap the coping down to be sure that it is in place before the deck is poured.

20. Pour the deck area, following the patio instructions in Unit 22. Figure 23-5, page 189, shows the deck area ready to be poured with wire mesh and a grid constructed of Number 4 reinforcement rods. Work the concrete into the bullnose of the vinyl coping. Finish the deck and the patio area in the desired finish. Score the deck with a groover to provide expansion joints, figure 23-6, page 189. (*Scoring* is to mark with lines or scratches across a surface with a steel instrument.) The expansion joints also serve as a decorative feature.

 CAUTION: The deck surface should be finished in a rough, nonskid finish.

21. Install the diving board standards and the ladder while the concrete is wet, figure 23-7.

✗ **CAUTION:** Be sure that the anchoring hardware is level and plumb.

22. Set the circulator pump in place and make the final plumbing hookup.

23. Clean the entire area and remove all debris.

24. Waterproof and seal the floor.

    A. Hose the pool floor. Remove the water with a sump pump.

    B. Etch the floor with a diluted solution of 18-percent muriatic acid, following booklet instructions. (To *etch* is to produce an effect with an acid.)

    C. Hose down the floor to remove the acid and neutralize the concrete. Pump all water out of the pool with a sump pump.

    D. Apply a 1/8-inch coat of waterproof seal. Be sure to follow the manufacturer's directions.

25. After the seal has dried, remove the taped seal and cloth from the drain and fill the pool.

✗ **CAUTION:** Refer to the manufacturer's instructions on the sealing compound to determine how long the seal should be left to dry before the pool is filled.

There are numerous manufacturers of pool kits. Because of this, only very general instructions have been given. It is imperative that the contractor carefully follow specific pool instructions.

APPLICATION

Complete each statement with the correct word or words.

1. The _____ at the edge of a pool is above the surrounding area so that surface water from the pool drains away from the pool.

2. A (an) _____ (is) are used to check the pool depth at various points as excavation of the site is done.

3. The deep end of a swimming pool has a (an) _____ which gradually slopes toward the deeper area.

4. When constructing a pool, the main drain is stuffed with _____ and taped closed until the final finish coat is applied.

5. The entire pool area is reinforced with _____.

6. _____ are bolted to each section of panels to hold them upright.

7. _____ (is) are placed in the tubes at the back of the panels and driven to the required depth.

8. A rim of concrete is placed around the outside edge of the pool to act as a (an) _____.

9. When packing a pool, pack the _____ end first and work toward the _____ end.

10. Before the pool is filled, the deck area is brushed with a (an) _____ to produce a porous, rough surface.

Section 7

Floor, Sidewalk, and Driveway Forms

Unit 24   Slipforming for Suspended Floors

OBJECTIVES

After studying this unit, the student will be able to

- list materials used in slipforming.
- construct slip forms for a suspended floor.

Suspended concrete floors are used in residential construction to more effectively use the floor space in the basement area. A *suspended floor* is a concrete slab supported by the concrete walls of a basement. Suspended floors in residential construction are usually constructed as a garage floor, with the area below the garage utilized as part of the basement. This type of floor is more expensive to construct than a conventional framed wooden floor. However, concrete is the only material which is practical and, at the same time, strong enough for a garage floor.

While forms can be built for a suspended floor, prefabricated forms are more practical. Prefabricated forms enable suspended construction to be performed much easier and with minimal use of dimensional and sheet forming stock. A series of reusable retractable beams which can be adjusted for various floor sizes are available.

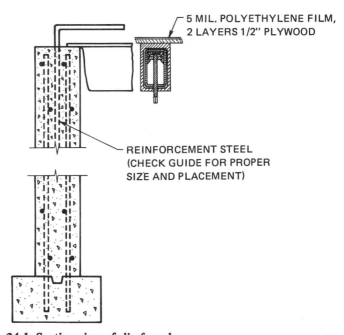

Fig. 24-1 Section view of slip form beam.

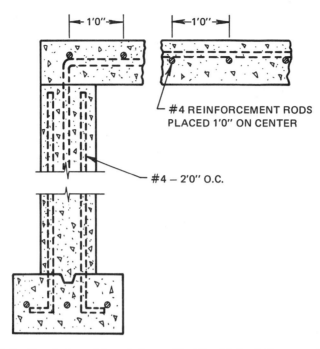

Fig. 24-2 Sectional view of foundation wall with added reinforcement rod.

Figure 24-1, page 193, shows a cross-sectional view of a slip form beam and platform materials prepared for the pouring of a suspended floor. (A *slip form,* or *sliding form,* is a form which moves during the placing of the concrete. It is usually used on large construction projects.)

Conventional basement walls should be reinforced with additional materials to support the suspended floor, figure 24-2. Suspended floors may be constructed for a one-, one and one half- or two-car garage; therefore, the size and spacing of reinforcing rods change to provide the required structural strength for various floor sizes. Figure 24-3 is a guide for determining reinforcement rod size and spacing for various sizes of suspended floors.

Figure 24-3				
GUIDE FOR REINFORCEMENT RODS FOR SUSPENDED GARAGE FLOORS*				
FLOOR SIZE			**ROD SIZE**	**ROD SPACING**
thickness	width	length		
4″	14′	24′	#4 - 1/2″	12″ O.C.**
5″	18′	24′	#5 - 5/8″	15″ O.C.**
6″	20′	24′	#5 - 5/8″	18″ O.C.***
6″	24′	24′	#6 - 3/4″	18″ O.C.***

*all 8" basement walls and reinforced as illustrated in figure 24-2.
**R.R. supported by 1" (SB) slab bolsters
***R.R. supported by 1 1/2" (SB) slab bolsters

Concrete for a suspended floor must be stronger than that which is used for the usual **floor** and must conform to certain specifications. Compressive strength should be 3,500 psi

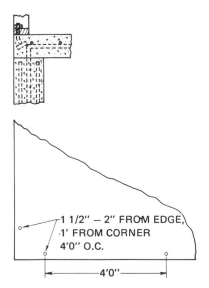

Fig. 24-4 Location of anchor bolts.

with a maximum slump of 3 inches. Coarse aggregate should be 3/4 inch. Care must be exercised when placing the concrete to be sure that no voids or air pockets remain. The concrete should be placed slowly and spread evenly over the area to prevent excessive pressure in any one area.

Garage walls must be attached directly to the suspended floor; therefore, anchor bolts must be placed in the plastic concrete to tie the walls in place. A 1/2-inch machine bolt may be used for this purpose. The bolt should have a 30-degree offset bend and should be positioned so that the bend is 1 inch below the finished surface of the floor when the bolt is placed, figure 24-4. The length of the anchor bolts varies with the depth or thickness of the floor.

Preparation for constructing a suspended floor must begin when the footing forms are constructed. The footing for a suspended garage floor should be 1 foot thick to accomodate an 8-inch wall. The additional thickness provides the compressive strength which is required to support the additional weight of the suspended floor. The actual procedure involved in placing the slip form beams and the preparation for placing the floor is detailed in the following steps.

SLIPFORMING A SUSPENDED FLOOR

1. Place retractable or adjustable metal beams on top of the concrete walls. The beams are designed so that each end fits halfway across the top of the wall. They should be set in position at 2-foot intervals and adjusted so that the top of the plywood is parallel with the top of the wall.

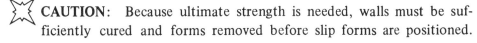 CAUTION: Because ultimate strength is needed, walls must be sufficiently cured and forms removed before slip forms are positioned.

2. Place two layers of 1/2-inch x 4-foot x 8-foot plywood sheets on top of the beams. Nail the two layers together to hold them in place. Care

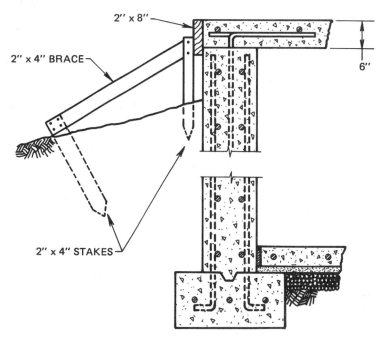

Fig. 24-5 Perimeter forms and bracing.

must be exercised in the layout to avoid joints in the first and second layer falling in the same position.

Note: The layout should be carefully arranged to minimize the number of sheets which must be cut; however, two layers are required to support the weight of the plastic concrete.

3. Place a 5 mill thick polyethylene plastic sheet over the plywood. The polyethylene film retains the wetness of the plastic concrete and prevents loss of liquid in the concrete as the floor is being placed.

4. Set the perimeter forms for the floor in place, figure 24-5. Perimeter forms are constructed of dimensional stock wide enough to fit against the outside edge of the foundation wall and extend above the top of the wall a distance equal to the thickness of the floor. For example, perimeter forms should extend 6 inches above the wall for a floor that is 6 inches thick.

   Level the top of the forms. If the top of the dimensional stock is set at the level of the floor thickness, the concrete may be screeded, using the top of the form as a thickness guide. Brace the perimeter forms at approximately 4-foot intervals to prevent buckling. Braces should be constructed in the same way as braces for wall forms are.

5. After the perimeter forms are set in place and the platform and polyethylene sheet are in position, place the reinforcement rods according to the size and spacing listed in figure 24-3, page 194. Care must be taken not to puncture or tear the polyethylene sheet.

A. Place reinforcement rods crosswise to transfer the stress created by the weight of the floor to the basement walls which are closest together. Reinforcement rods for the floor should be tied with wire to the wall reinforcement rods, which have been bent down in place at a 90-degree angle.

B. Place reinforcement rods lengthwise. Tie the rods at each end to the wall reinforcement rods.

    Note: Reinforcement rods are positioned 1 1/2 to 2 inches above the plywood so that they are embedded in the concrete.

C. Tie the reinforcement rods at each intersection to form an appropriately sized grid. For example, a 20-foot x 24-foot floor requires an 18-inch square grid.

6. Run the first layer of concrete about one half the thickness of the floor. Keep an even flow of materials and spread it evenly as it is being placed. Be sure that the concrete flows evenly under and around the reinforcement rods. To avoid an excessive amount being screeded off and wasted, a second layer of concrete should be placed immediately. This concrete should be worked across the narrow width and screeded as closely as possible to the placing operation.

 CAUTION: Consolidate or vibrate the concrete as it is poured to prevent air pockets or voids. This is especially important in a suspended floor where great strength is required.

7. Float the concrete as soon as the surface water begins to disappear from the surface of the concrete.

8. Place the anchor bolts 1 foot from each end and 4 feet on center. Float the entire area.

9. Trowel the area to the desired finish. The floor may be colored at this point with a colored powder. The powder is troweled into the finished surface.

    Note: A trowel or float may be used. If a trowel is used, however, guard against creating a slick and dangerous floor.

10. Allow the concrete to cure. The floor should be cured slowly; therefore, attention must be paid to weather conditions on the job. In hot weather, keep the floor damp and covered for the first three days. This can be accomplished by covering the floor with moist burlap. Under extremely cold conditions, heat may be required to prevent the concrete from freezing. Concrete reaches about 80 percent of its ultimate strength in seven days; therefore, as a general rule, forms for a suspended floor should not be removed for seven days.

11. Remove the forms.

A. Remove the support beams by retracting the movable end into the center chamber. Two workers should accomplish this, since the plywood will begin to fall as soon as the removal of the beams progresses past the first joints in the plywood platform.

> *Note:* The open spaces which remain where the beams were positioned may be filled with mortar if desired. The finishing methods used on the walls may determine whether or not the spaces are filled.

B. Remove the perimeter forms.

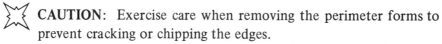 **CAUTION:** Exercise care when removing the perimeter forms to prevent cracking or chipping the edges.

C. Clean and oil the dimensional and sheet stock if it is to be used again for suspended floor forms.

APPLICATION

Complete each statement with the correct word or words.

1. The platform for a suspended floor is supported by _____.

2. The floor of the platform is composed of _____ layers of 1/2-inch plywood.

3. Care should be exercised when placing the plywood sheets to ensure that the _____ in the first and second layers do not fall in the same place.

4. Polyethlene film placed over the plywood is _____ in thickness.

5. Suspended floors should be reinforced with Number _____ or _____ reinforcement rods, depending upon the area.

6. Exterior side forms are made of _____-inch dimensional stock.

7. A Number 5 reinforcement rod is _____ in diameter.

8. A suspended floor is _____ (more, less) expensive than conventional floor framing.

9. Reinforcement rods around the perimeter of the supporting walls serve as _____ or _____ for the suspended floor.

10. Concrete must be carefully _____ as it is poured to prevent air pockets or voids which weaken the structural strength.

Unit 25   Slab and Basement Floors

OBJECTIVES

After studying this unit, the student will be able to

- identify the materials used to pour a basement or slab floor.
- list the steps involved in pouring a slab at grade level.
- list the steps involved in pouring a basement floor.

Generally, there are two types of concrete floors used in residential construction. These are slab floors which are poured directly on top of the soil at surface elevation, and basement floors which are poured below ground level, figure 25-1. A well-drained area and an adequate footing which extends below the frost line are necessary for either the slab or basement floor.

SLAB CONSTRUCTION

A number of factors must be considered before a slab floor is poured at ground level. The topography, type of soil, and climate are all determining factors when pouring a dry, stable slab floor.

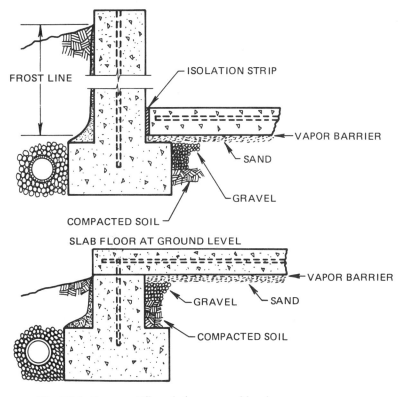

Fig. 25-1 Basement floor below ground level.

The elevation of a particular building site is very important in relation to the ability of the moisture in the soil to evaporate. A great amount of rain, spring thaws, melting snow, or drainage of adjacent areas may all increase the possibility of flooding.

It is also important to consider the type of soil at the building site. As previously discussed, some soils, such as coarse sand, drain well while soils such as clay retain moisture and become slippery when wet. If the soil is moisture retaining and the area drains poorly, a structure built on a low foundation is a better choice than a slab. If a slab floor is constructed, proper drainage methods and insulation procedures should be followed very carefully.

Climatic conditions of a particular area must also be considered. A location in Florida where frost penetration is minimal is not subjected to freezing and thawing conditions found in Minnesota.

The footing and foundation for a slab at ground level is essentially the same as those for other structures. The footing must be sufficiently wide and thick to support the structure. It is also essential that the footings be located below frost level to prevent heaving. Whether or not a foundation wall is needed depends on the frost depth. However, because most areas do have some frost penetration, a foundation wall is usually poured between the footing and the ground level, figure 25-2. The slab itself is poured after the footing and foundation have cured; therefore, only perimeter forms are needed.

How to Construct a Slab Floor

1. Level the foundation area with a bulldozer or grader. Use a builder's level or transit to ensure that the area is level.

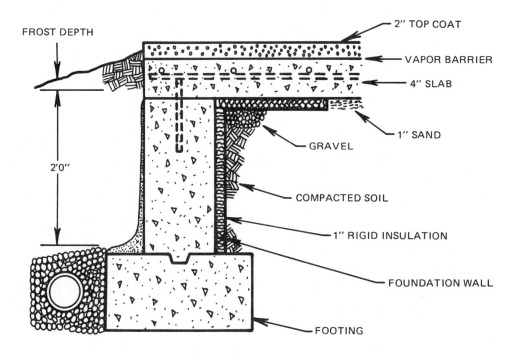

Fig. 25-2 Slab with footing set below frost level.

2. Lay out and stake the perimeter of the house.

   CAUTION: Check local building codes to verify the location on the lot.

3. Excavate 4 inches of topsoil from the building site. The earth under the floor must be solid and completely free of tree roots and debris.

4. Dig a trench around the perimeter of the house to the depth and width which is required for the footing and foundation wall, plus an allowance for working room.

5. Pour the footing and foundation wall. The foundation wall should be 8 inches above the grade line so that the wooden structure does not touch the ground.

   CAUTION: Always install drain tile as explained in Unit 4. If the area is unusually wet, cross tile as well as perimeter tile should be installed.

6. Fill the excavated area with a layer of coarse gravel or crushed stone. Tamp the gravel firmly. The fill material should be coarse so that there are air spaces in the fill area. This reduces moisture and provides insulation.

7. Place drain tile around the outside edge of the exterior wall footing.

8. Install all utility lines. Be sure that the connections are above the finished concrete level, figure 25-3.

Fig. 25-3 Utility lines installed in preparation for pouring of the floor.
Courtesy of Mid Missouri Company

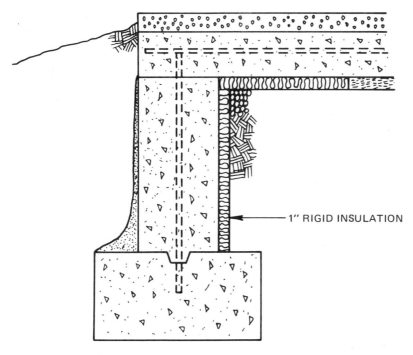

1" RIGID INSULATION

Fig. 25-4 Perimeter insulation.

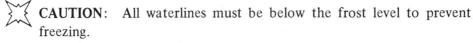 **CAUTION:** All waterlines must be below the frost level to prevent freezing.

9. Place a vapor barrier over the fill. The vapor barrier may be asphaltum-impregnated paper, roofing material, or special heavy polyethylene film. Each strip should be overlapped about 6 inches to ensure that moisture does not seep through to the slab.

   Note: Always carefully follow the manufacturer's instructions which accompany the vapor barrier. Be sure that the vapor barrier is not torn. These are important steps since water must be kept from the slab.

10. Install perimeter insulation 1 to 2 inches thick, figure 25-4. This is a rigid material that can tolerate the pressure of wet concrete. The insulation is installed so that heat does not escape in the place where the wall and slab meet.

11. Lay the reinforcing material in place. Use either Number 10-gage wire mesh measuring 6 inches x 6 inches or 1/2-inch reinforcement rods placed to form 12-inch grids. If reinforcement rods are used, they should be tied at intersections to prevent them from slipping. A light structure such as a single-story ranch house usually requires only a 4-inch slab; however, local building codes should always be checked to determine slab thickness in a given area. Reinforcement material should be approximately 1 to 1 1/2 inches from the top surface of the slab.

12. Pour the concrete, consolidating it as it is poured to prevent air pockets. The concrete mix should have a maximum slump range of 2 to 5 inches. In most cases, the lower the slump factor is, the higher the quality of the concrete is.

    Note: Be sure that the concrete is distributed evenly as it is poured.

13. Screed the concrete off to the correct level.

14. Place the anchoring devices, usually 4 to 8 feet O.C.

    CAUTION: Always check building codes to determine anchoring requirements for a given area. Areas prone to hurricanes require stronger anchoring methods than other areas. Slab structures are frequently constructed in hurricane areas.

15. Finish the surface as soon as the surface moisture disappears.

    A. Float the surface. For air-entrained concrete, use an aluminum or magnesium float. Standard concrete can be floated with a wooden float.

       Note: Always begin in the driest area.

    B. Trowel the surface. This operation should be performed on areas where the concrete surface is to be used as the actual finished surface or where a resilient type of flooring, such as vinyl tile, is to be installed. Trowel the surface.

16. Allow the concrete to cure. Weather conditions and the concrete mixture determines necessary measures for curing the concrete.

    A. If the temperature is high and the area exposed to the sun, the concrete is kept damp and is covered the first three days.

    B. If there are high, warm winds, the concrete should be covered with a damp cloth or a windbreak should be constructed to prevent overly rapid drying of the surface area. (A *windbreak* is used to shelter a work area from the wind.)

    C. If it is rainy, place a waterproof cover over the surface until the concrete has set.

    D. In subtemperatures, use concrete with admixtures designed for cold weather. An external heating or insulating system may also be used.

BASEMENT FLOORS

Basement floors are poured in much the same way as slab floors. They are usually poured after the structure has been framed; in this way, the floor is not exposed to the weather. A 4-inch floor is usually sufficient unless the structure is quite large; in those cases, a 6-inch floor is preferred. Basement floors are separated from the foundation by a 1/2-inch isolation strip. This enables the basement floor to float free of the foundation, thus preventing cracks or breaks if heaving should occur.

How to Construct a Basement Floor

1. Determine the finished floor elevation by measuring from the top of the foundation or ceiling level to the floor surface. Mark the finished floor level on the foundation wall by snapping a chalk line along the surface line.

   ✦ **CAUTION:** Use a builder's level to ensure that the surface is level.

2. Be sure that the original soil is compacted and free of tree roots and debris.

3. Fill the area with large crushed gravel or limestone to a point within 4 to 6 inches of the surface line. This provides insulation and prevents capillary moisture from reaching the floor.

   Note: The area should be excavated deeply enough to allow at least 4 inches of gravel fill.

4. Install all utility lines. Bring the connections above the finished surface level.

   Note: Perimeter drain tile has already been installed. However, if the area is unusually wet, drain tile may be placed across the surface under the fill material as well.

5. Install the vapor barrier. The vapor barrier can be 4 to 5 mil polyethylene film, asphaltum-impregnated paper, or roofing material. Strips should be overlapped approximately 6 inches.

   Note: Always follow manufacturer's installation directions as they may vary somewhat.

6. Brush a strip of asphaltum on the foundation. Press the vapor barrier against the asphaltum to seal it. Place a 1/2-inch x 4-inch asphalt-impregnated felt isolation strip along the perimeter.

   ✦ **CAUTION:** Do not extend the asphaltum above the surface line.

7. Install the rigid perimeter insulation strip to prevent heat from escaping at the point where the wall and floor meet. The strip should extend 2 feet under the floor and up the wall to the surface.

8. Position the reinforcement rods. Ten-gage, 6-inch wire mesh or Number 4 reinforcement rods may be used. If reinforcement rods are used, form 12-inch grids and tie them at intersections to prevent slippage. The reinforcement steel should be approximately 1 1/2 inches from the surface.

9. Pour the concrete through a window, fireplace, or stair opening. Contractors usually purchase ready-mixed concrete from a concrete dealer who delivers the concrete mix to the job site in a truck.

10. Finish the concrete.

    A. Screed the concrete to the surface level using a 2-inch x 4-inch board.

B. Float the surface as soon as it has been screeded, using a bull float or darby.

Note: Use a magnesium metal float for air-entrained mixes. Other mixes may be floated with a wooden or metal float.

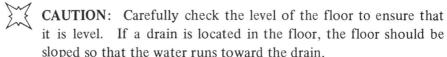

CAUTION: Carefully check the level of the floor to ensure that it is level. If a drain is located in the floor, the floor should be sloped so that the water runs toward the drain.

11. Allow the concrete to cure. If the floor is in an enclosed area, keep the area moist for three days with wet burlap, or dampen the slab once or twice a day.

APPLICATION

Complete each statement with the correct word or words.

1. The footing for a basement foundation or a slab on grade level must be below the _____.

2. Fill material under basement and slab floors consist of _____ or _____.

3. The fill provides insulation and prevents _____ from entering the slab.

4. Fill is covered with a (an) _____.

5. Fill is _____ to _____ inch (inches) deep.

6. A slab or basement is usually _____ inch (inches) deep.

7. To prevent the escaping of heat between the foundation wall and the slab or floor, a rigid _____ is installed around the perimeter.

8. An asphaltum-impregnated _____ is placed between the wall and the floor or slab so that the floor is not tied to the wall. This eliminates the danger of cracks caused by shifting soil or heaving.

9. Vapor barrier strips should overlap approximately _____ inch (inches) to ensure that moisture does not seep through.

10. As soon as the surface moisture has evaporated, the floor may be _____.

Unit 26　Sidewalk and Driveway Forms

OBJECTIVES

After studying this unit, the student will be able to

- identify materials used in sidewalk and driveway construction.
- list steps involved in constructing sidewalk and driveway forms.
- construct sidewalk and driveway forms.

Sidewalks and driveways are the last concrete jobs to be completed. They are usually constructed after the residential structure has been completed. They may be placed by the builder or the foundation contractor. If the area has had extensive fill work, the finish grade should be established and thoroughly settled before the sidewalk and driveway are poured. If the fill has not settled, the shifting and settling of the fill material causes the concrete to crack and break.

SIDEWALKS

Service walks are usually 3 feet wide; main entrances are usually 4 feet wide. Both are usually 4 inches thick. In wet or damp areas, the sidewalk area is filled with a coarse, granular fill such as coarse gravel or crushed stone. However, if the area drains well, the sidewalk can be poured directly on the ground, which should be compacted and free of roots and other debris.

The sidewalk should float free of the foundation. This helps prevent cracking or breaking if the ground shifts or settles under the sidewalk. Sidewalks do not require reinforcement. However, they should either be scored or have expansion joints placed at approximate 4- to 5-foot invervals to allow room for expansion caused by climatic conditions. Sidewalks should be sloped 1/8 to 1/4 inch per foot to ensure adequate drainage. The sidewalk should also be rounded off at the edge so that the edge does not crumble or chip.

Construction Procedures

1. Lay out and stake the sidewalk area.
2. Excavate the area to a 4-inch depth and compact the soil.
3. Set the forms in place. Pieces of lumber measuring 2 inches x 4 inches are usually used for sidewalk forms; however, commercial forms are also available, figure 26-1, page 207. Nail the forms to stakes placed on the outside of the form every 3 to 4 feet with duplex-head nails. Check to be sure that the forms are level. One side of the form should be lower than the other to provide a 1/8- to 1/4-inch slope per foot for adequate drainage.
4. Place an isolation strip of asphaltum-impregnated felt 1/2 inch thick against the foundation.

Fig. 26-1 Slab form which may be used for floor slab, driveway, or sidewalk work.
Courtesy of Proctor Products, Incorporated

5. Place the concrete. Distribute and consolidate it as it is being placed. Air-entrained concrete is used because sidewalks are constantly being exposed to the elements. The slump should be 4 inches.

6. Using a piece of lumber 2 inches x 4 inches, screed the concrete off to the level of the forms.

7. As soon as the surface moisture has evaporated, float the surface so that the larger aggregate is below the surface and the desired finish is obtained.

   Note: Since a sidewalk should have a somewhat rough texture for better footing, troweling is not usually necessary.

8. With a groover, create a groove every 4 to 6 feet. This provides room for expansion and contraction of the slab and eliminates surface cracks. Alternate methods may also be used.

   Note: An isolation strip of 1/2-inch asphaltum-impregnated felt may be placed in the wet concrete, or the groove may be cut with a masonry saw approximately two days after the concrete has been poured.

9. Using an edger, round off the edge of the sidewalk so that it does not chip or crumble.

10. Cover the sidewalk with damp burlap for three days to keep the surface moist. This enables the concrete to cure properly and prevents *crazing* (small surface cracks) as the concrete cures.

11. Remove the forms and fill in the excavated area. The area may be filled with loose gravel rather than topsoil if preferred. When loose gravel is used, there is a narrow band on each side of the walk free of grass. The sidewalk may be used for light traffic as soon as the forms are removed, but should not be subjected to normal traffic before the seventh day. Concrete reaches 80 to 90 percent of its design strength after 28 days so caution should be exercised in the use of the walk for the first month.

DRIVEWAYS

Driveways must be constructed to handle a great amount of weight. Reinforcement rods or mesh are always used in driveways. Concrete which is 4 inches thick is strong enough for passenger cars; however, if a driveway is to be used regularly by oil delivery trucks or refuse trucks, it should be 6 inches thick. A single drive should be 12 feet wide; a double drive should be 20 feet in width. As in sidewalk construction, the subgrade of driveways in damp areas or areas subjected to freezing is excavated deeper than 4 inches. It is then filled with coarse granular fill which is compacted before the concrete is poured. Driveways should also float free of the garage or foundation and have expansion joints every 8 to 10 feet to prevent cracking and breaking.

Forms for driveways are constructed of lumber measuring 2 inches x 4 inches or 2 inches x 6 inches, depending on the required thickness. Slab forms such as the form in figure 26-1, page 207, may also be used. The driveway should slope away from the structure toward the street approximately 1/8 inch per foot for adequate drainage. If the driveway actually slopes toward the structure from the street, as it does in a house with a basement garage, the driveway must have a cross slope so that it drains away from the house.

Air-entrained concrete should be used for driveways since they are exposed to the elements.

Construction Procedures

1. Lay out and stake the driveway.

    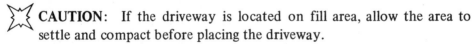 **CAUTION:** If the driveway is located on fill area, allow the area to settle and compact before placing the driveway.

2. Excavate the driveway area.

3. Set the forms in place using lumber measuring 2 inches x 4 inches or 2 inches x 6 inches nailed to stakes. Commercial forms may also be used. Follow the manufacturer's instructions when using commercial forms. Stakes should be placed every 3 to 5 feet on the outside of the forms and attached with duplex-head nails for easy removal.

    CAUTION: Slope the forms toward the street approximately 1/8 inch per foot so that the driveway drains away from the structure. If the street is on a higher level than the garage entrance, the slope should be toward one side.

4. Place an isolation strip of 1/2-inch asphaltum-impregnated felt along the foundation of the structure so that the driveway floats free of the structure.

   Note: Paint a strip of asphaltum along the foundation so that the isolation strip adheres to the surface and does not shift under the pressure of the wet concrete.

5. Install Number 10-gage 6-inch wire mesh for reinforcement.

6. Place the concrete in one operation, evenly distributing it and consolidating it as it is poured. The concrete next to the building is placed first so that the isolation strip is held in place.

7. Screed the concrete level with the form.

8. Place the expansion strips if 1-inch x 4-inch expansion strips are used. The strips should be placed every 8 to 10 feet. Redwood is an ideal wood for this use. If the driveway is more than 12 feet wide, an expansion joint is placed down the center. If the expansion joints are to be scored, use a groover to score 1 inch deep after the surface has been floated.

9. Float the surface with a large bull float. This is the only finish required for a driveway since a rough surface texture is desired.

   Note: A magnesium or aluminum float is used on air-entrained concrete.

10. Round the edge with an edger to prevent it from chipping.

    Note: If the expansion joints are to be scored, they are scored at this point. Joints may also be cut with a masonry saw after the concrete has set.

11. Place damp burlap over the surface and keep it damp for three days to cure the concrete.

12. Carefully remove the forms after the third day. Do not use the driveway for approximately a week to enable the concrete to reach its ultimate strength.

13. Fill the excavated area with soil, crushed stone, or gravel.

ESTIMATING CONCRETE

The formula for estimating the amount of concrete needed for a driveway or sidewalk is:

$$\frac{\text{length (feet) x width (feet) x thickness (feet)}}{27} = \text{cubic yards}$$

Therefore, the concrete needed for a sidewalk which is 4 inches thick, 4 feet wide, and 40 feet long is

$$\frac{40' \times 4' \times 1/3'}{27} = \frac{1 \times 4 \times 40}{3 \times 27} = \frac{160}{81} = 1.975 \text{ or 2 cubic yards}$$

APPLICATION

Complete each statement with the correct word or words.

1. A sidewalk is _____ to _____ feet wide.

2. Sidewalk or driveways which are subjected to damp soil or frost penetration are filled with _____-inch coarse gravel.

3. The edges of a sidewalk or driveway are rounded with a (an) _____.

4. _____ is the ideal wood to be used for expansion joints.

5. Sidewalk expansion joints should be placed every _____ to _____ feet.

6. A (an) _____ should always be placed between the structure foundation and the sidewalk or driveway.

7. _____ concrete is the best concrete to use for a driveway or sidewalk since they are constantly exposed to the elements.

8. The maximum size aggregate for a 4-inch thick sidewalk is _____.

9. Driveways are _____ to _____ inch (inches) thick, depending upon the expected traffic.

10. Expansion joints may be scored using a (an) _____ or a (an) _____.

Appendix

Table I   Common English Measurement Conversion

Linear Measure		
12 inches (in.)	=	1 foot (ft.)
3 feet	=	1 yard (yd.)
Surface Measure		
144 sq. in.	=	1 sq. ft.
9 sq. ft.	=	1 sq. yd.
Cubic Measure		
1728 cu. in.	=	1 cu. ft.
27 cu. ft.	=	1 cu. yd.

Table II   Fractional and Decimal Equivalents to Millimeters

Inches	Decimal Equivalents In Inches	Millimeters	Inches	Decimal Equivalents In Inches	Millimeters
1/64	.015625	0.397	33/64	.515625	13.097
1/32	.03125	0.794	17/32	.53125	13.494
3/64	.046875	1.191	35/64	.546875	13.890
1/16	.0625	1.587	9/16	.5625	14.287
5/64	.078125	1.984	37/64	.578125	14.684
3/32	.09375	2.381	19/32	.59375	15.081
7/64	.109375	2.778	39/64	.609375	15.478
1/8	.125	3.175	5/8	.625	15.875
9/64	.140625	3.572	41/64	.640625	16.272
5/32	.15625	3.969	21/32	.65625	16.669
11/64	.171875	4.366	43/64	.671875	17.065
3/16	.1875	4.762	11/16	.6875	17.462
13/64	.203125	5.159	45/64	.703125	17.859
7/32	.21875	5.556	23/32	.71875	18.256
15/64	.234375	5.953	47/64	.734375	18.653
1/4	.25	6.350	3/4	.75	19.050
17/64	.265625	6.747	49/64	.765625	19.447
9/32	.28125	7.144	25/32	.78125	19.844
19/64	.296875	7.541	51/64	.796875	20.240
5/16	.3125	7.937	13/16	.8125	20.637
21/64	.328125	8.334	53/64	.828125	21.034
11/32	.34375	8.731	27/32	.84375	21.431
23/64	.359375	9.128	55/64	.859375	21.828
3/8	.375	9.525	7/8	.875	22.225
25/64	.390625	9.922	57/64	.890625	22.622
13/32	.40625	10.319	29/32	.90625	23.019
27/64	.421875	10.716	59/64	.921875	23.415
7/16	.4375	11.113	15/16	.9375	23.812
29/64	.453125	11.509	61/64	.953125	24.209
15/32	.46875	11.906	31/32	.96875	24.606
31/64	.484375	12.303	63/64	.984375	25.003
1/2	.5	12.700	1	1	25.400

Table III Millimeters to Decimal Inches

Mm In.	Mm In.	Mm In.	Mm In.	Mm In.
1 = 0.0394	21 = 0.8268	41 = 1.6142	61 = 2.4016	81 = 3.1890
2 = 0.0787	22 = 0.8662	42 = 1.6536	62 = 2.4410	82 = 3.2284
3 = 0.1181	23 = 0.9055	43 = 1.6929	63 = 2.4804	83 = 3.2678
4 = 0.1575	24 = 0.9449	44 = 1.7323	64 = 2.5197	84 = 3.3071
5 = 0.1969	25 = 0.9843	45 = 1.7717	65 = 2.5591	85 = 3.3465
6 = 0.2362	26 = 1.0236	46 = 1.8111	66 = 2.5985	86 = 3.3859
7 = 0.2756	27 = 1.0630	47 = 1.8504	67 = 2.6378	87 = 3.4253
8 = 0.3150	28 = 1.1024	48 = 1.8898	68 = 2.6772	88 = 3.4646
9 = 0.3543	29 = 1.1418	49 = 1.9292	69 = 2.7166	89 = 3.5040
10 = 0.3937	30 = 1.1811	50 = 1.9685	70 = 2.7660	90 = 3.5434
11 = 0.4331	31 = 1.2205	51 = 2.0079	71 = 2.7953	91 = 3.5827
12 = 0.4724	32 = 1.2599	52 = 2.0473	72 = 2.8247	92 = 3.6221
13 = 0.5118	33 = 1.2992	53 = 2.0867	73 = 2.8741	93 = 3.6615
14 = 0.5512	34 = 1.3386	54 = 2.1260	74 = 2.9134	94 = 3.7009
15 = 0.5906	35 = 1.3780	55 = 2.1654	75 = 2.9528	95 = 3.7402
16 = 0.6299	36 = 1.4173	56 = 2.2048	76 = 2.9922	96 = 3.7796
17 = 0.6693	37 = 1.4567	57 = 2.2441	77 = 3.0316	97 = 3.8190
18 = 0.7087	38 = 1.4961	58 = 2.2835	78 = 2.0709	98 = 3.8583
19 = 0.7480	39 = 1.5355	59 = 2.3229	79 = 3.1103	99 = 3.8977
20 = 0.7874	40 = 1.5748	60 = 2.3622	80 = 3.1497	100 = 3.9371

Table IV Metric Measure

Linear Measure		
Unit	Symbol or Abbreviation	Value in Meters
Millimeters	mm.	0.001
Centimeter	cm.	0.01
Decimeter	dm.	0.1
Meter	m.	1.0
Surface Measure		
Unit	Symbol or Abbreviation	Value in Sq. Meters
Square millimeter	$mm.^2$	0.000001
Square centimeter	$cm.^2$	0.0001
Square decimeter	$d.^2$	0.01
Square meter (centiare)	$m.^2$	1.0

Table 5 Architectural Symbols

IN SECTION

BRICK

STONE

CONCRETE

EARTH

ELECTRICAL

CEILING OUTLET

WALL BRACKET OUTLET

DUPLEX OUTLET

S_1 SWITCH (Single Pole)

S_3 3-WAY SWITCH

PLUMBING

COLD WATER

HOT WATER

ROLL RIM TUB

ANGLE TUB

SHOWER STALL

WATER CLOSET

BIDET

URINAL STALL TYPE

LAVATORY

KITCHEN SINK R & L DRAIN BOARD

COMBINATION SINK AND DISHWASHER

HWT HOT WATER TANK

M WATER METER

HOSE BIBB OR FAUCET

D DRAIN

R GAS RANGE

D DRYER

WM WASHING MACHINE

WALL—TYPE DRINKING FOUNTAIN

DW DRY WELL

WH WATER HEATER

HEATING AND VENTILATING

RAD RADIATOR EXPOSED

UNIT HEATER

UNIT VENTILATOR

TRAP THERMOSTATIC

TRAP – FLOAT AND THERMOSTAT

TRAP BOILER RETURN

VALVE AIR LINE

VALVE DIAPHRAGM

VALVE STRAINER

T THERMOSTAT

IN PLAN

EXTERIOR DOOR (In Wood Part)

WINDOW (In Wood Part)

WINDOW (In Brick Veneer)

WINDOW (In Brick Part)

METAL

RADIATOR

SUPPLY DUCT

RETURN DUCT

SUPPLY LINE

RETURN LINE

RISER

RETURN

Acknowledgments

CONTRIBUTIONS BY DELMAR STAFF

Publication Director – Alan N. Knofla

Series Editor – Mark W. Huth

Source Editor – Mary R. Grauerholz

Reviewers – John B. West, Ted Marotta

Director of Manufacturing and Production – Frederick Sharer

Production Specialists – Patti Manuli, Sharon Lynch, Jean LeMorta, Debbie Monty, Betty Michelfelder, Lee St. Onge, Margaret Mutka

Illustrators – Tony Canabush, Michael Kokernak, George Dowse

214

INDEX

A current catalog including prices of all Delmar educational
publications is available upon request. Please write to:

Catalog Department
Delmar Publishers Inc.
3 Columbia Circle
Box 15-015
Albany, NY 12212